THE TIMES TOP 100 GRADUATE EMPLOYERS

The definitive guide to the leading employers
recruiting graduates during 2005-2006.

HIGH FLIERS

**HIGH FLIERS PUBLICATIONS LTD
IN ASSOCIATION WITH THE TIMES**

Published by High Fliers Publications Limited
10a Belmont Street, Camden Town, London NW1 8HH
Telephone: 020 7428 9100   Web: www.Top100GraduateEmployers.com

Editor **Martin Birchall**
Publishing Manager **Gill Thomas**
Production Manager **Sean Fulton**
Portrait Photography **Robert Hollingworth** www.roberthollingworth.co.uk

The Times Top 100 Graduate Employers is based on research results from *The UK Graduate Careers Survey 2005,* produced by High Fliers Research Ltd.

The greatest care has been taken in compiling this book. However, no responsibility can be accepted by the publishers or compilers for the accuracy of the information presented.

Where opinion is expressed it is that of the author or advertiser and does not necessarily coincide with the editorial views of High Fliers Publications Limited or The Times newspaper.

Printed and bound in Great Britain by CPI Bath Press.

A CIP catalogue record for this book
is available from the British Library.
ISBN 0 9536991 6 1

Contents

Employer Entries

Information Request Service
Find out more about Britain's top employers and you could
win an iPod Shuffle or start your career £5,000 richer!

THE TIMES is read by 303,000 ABC1
aged 21-35 ► More than any other quality daily
THE TIMES
THURSDAYS
CAREER
15 PAGES OF THE BEST JOBS
...plus a weekly guide to enhancing your value 13.01.05
GRADUATE SPECIAL Looking good: the great jobs bonanza 11
► Spare a minute or two to read our guide to time management 10

Foreword

by Parminder Bahra
Career Editor, The Times

One of the things that will happen a year or so after you've secured your first graduate job is that you'll receive a statement from your pension plan provider. Amongst the financial jargon, you will come across a figure that says something like, "you have 44 years and three months of service before you can retire". That is a very long time, so it is somewhat of an understatement to suggest that the career choice you make now is important.

It is therefore my pleasure to welcome you to the new edition of *The Times Top 100 Graduate Employers* – your essential guide to the top employers who are recruiting graduates during 2005-2006. It is based entirely on the views of graduates who completed their degrees in 2005 and has been compiled from face-to-face interviews with more than 16,000 university-leavers, to provide a valuable insight into Britain's most desirable employers.

With forty-odd years of employment ahead, you will be pleased to hear there are many reasons for the 'Class of 2006' graduates to feel upbeat. The Association of Graduate Recruiters (AGR) has reported a substantial increase in graduate vacancies over the last two years, which means job numbers have risen by more than a fifth since 2003. In addition, in its most recent survey, a third of employers said they expect to step up their recruitment in 2006 and over half plan to at least match their 2005 intake.

There is good news on the remuneration front too. The AGR reports that the average starting salary for new graduates in 2005 is £22,000 from top employers, up nearly five per cent on the previous year. Furthermore, at least a third of firms offered a 'starting work' bonus compared with a quarter from the previous year. The report also found that two per cent of employers plan to give more than £5,000 to their new recruits as a joining bonus.

This may however reflect the increasing costs involved in completing an undergraduate degree. There is a lot at stake. The cost of studying is at a record high – *The UK Graduate Careers Survey 2005* reported average graduation debts in 2005 of £10,400. And future generations will have the controversial 'top-up' tuition fees to consider too.

But if you have ever wondered why you chose to do a degree, then consider the findings of new research from Swansea University. It shows that a typical degree holder will earn around £150,000 more than someone with just A-levels during their career, and for some subjects such as maths or IT the difference could be as large as £225,000. It seems that a degree can be a very worthwhile investment.

Having said that, you have told us that it is not just about money. Of the characteristics that were important to the 'Class of 2005', 84 per cent wanted to work for a socially responsible employer; 77 per cent expected to join an employer that is environmentally aware; but just 32 per cent hope to join an organisation that "would make your friends envious".

The media industry still heads up the list of sectors that the most graduates have applied for. But while 12.7 per cent are looking to work in the sector, only 0.6 per cent of vacancies at the leading employers were for media jobs.

Nevertheless, the choice of employment for the 'Class of 2006' is a wide one with over 1,000 national or international employers planning to recruit from Britain's universities during 2005-2006.

The world of work changes continuously. As a small boy, my generation was told that one of our biggest headaches would be what we would do with our leisure time. Robotic technology would do all our work for us leaving us with endless amounts of spare time on our hands. Instead, the reality is that we are working longer hours now than we ever have done. We juggle cappuccinos with laptops while tapping out emails on Blackberrys on our way to the next meeting. It seems sometimes as if the technology is in charge of us rather than the other way around.

While on the one hand I feel slightly short-changed, on the other, I am also aware of the incredible opportunities that the modern workplace offers. Our jobs now encompass worldwide travel, career development and training, all manner of company perks and of course there's always the odd free lunch in a fine restaurant.

With these more tempting offers comes greater competition. There are record numbers of graduates entering the jobs market. An estimated 260,000 graduates are expected to leave university in 2006, up from less than 200,000 ten years ago.

Graduate job hunting is not an easy process, particularly because much of it happens at just the same time as revision for final exams or crucial degree coursework. The aim of *The Times Top 100 Graduate Employers* is to showcase the very best employment opportunities available for graduates this year.

For those who are looking to get the best possible head start to their careers, this book provides invaluable information on employers' vacancies, application deadlines and details of their graduate development schemes.

So, I wish you all the best of luck in securing the positions that you seek and hope you have a fulfiling 44 years and three months of working life ahead.

Parminder Bahra is editor of Career, *the weekly jobs section published every Thursday in The Times.*

Feed your mind.

How would you like your career – well done?

Fed a diet of first-class training, top-drawer clients and innumerable opportunities to excel, both as an individual and within a team, and it's easy to see a career at Deloitte is something worth getting your teeth into.

As the fastest growing professional services firm, we can offer you unparalleled career opportunities to stimulate and reward your grey matter. Our training and development schemes for graduates are first class and, thanks to the uniquely collaborative way in which we work, you'll participate in team projects that draw on expertise and experience from across the firm's key service areas of audit, tax, consulting and corporate finance. There are a number of undergraduate opportunities on offer as well, from our Summer vacation schemes to our Insight days which showcase what working at Deloitte is really like.

If you've been predicted or obtained a 2:1 and have at least 300 UCAS tariff points under your belt, visit **www.deloitte.co.uk/graduates** where you'll find plenty more information to chew on.

We recruit from any discipline, welcome applications for deferred entry and recruit nationwide.

Deloitte.

Audit. Tax. Consulting. Corporate Finance.

www.ideas.astrazeneca.com

Graduate opportunities, all disciplines.

If you're a graduate with outstanding talent, you'll never be just another face in the crowd at AstraZeneca. Our approach to development is focused on giving you the attention you need to reach your potential – and rewarding your performance as an individual. So if you're looking for the recognition you deserve, visit **www.ideas.astrazeneca.com**

Compiling the Top 100 Graduate Employers

by Martin Birchall
Survey Director, High Fliers Research Ltd

Students in the final year of a degree course or graduates who have recently left university certainly have a wide choice of prospective employers at the moment. The number of job vacancies for graduates has increased for two consecutive years and there are expected to be over five thousand organisations recruiting new talent from UK universities during 2005-2006.

Such a huge choice can make selecting the employer that is 'right' for you much more difficult. How should you evaluate all the different opportunities and what determines which employers offer the best graduate positions? What are the main criteria that you can use to assess so many organisations and jobs?

There are no simple answers to these questions and clearly no one employer can ever hope to be right for every graduate – everyone makes their own judgements about the organisations they want to work for and the type of job they find the most attractive.

So how, then, can anyone produce a meaningful league table of the leading employers? What criteria can define whether one organisation is 'better' than another? To compile *The Times Top 100 Graduate Employers*, the independent market research company, High Fliers Research Ltd, interviewed 16,113 final year students who left UK universities in the summer of 2005. The students from the 'Class of 2005'

who took part in the study were selected at random to represent the full cross-section of finalists at their universities, not just those who had already secured graduate employment. The research examined students experiences during their search for a graduate job and asked them about their attitudes to employers.

The key question used to produce the *Top 100* was "Which employer do you think offers the best opportunities for graduates?" This question was deliberately open-ended and students were not prompted in any way. Across the whole survey, finalists mentioned more than 350 different organisations – from the smallest local employers, to some of the world's best-known companies. The responses were analysed to identify the number of times each employer was mentioned. The one hundred organisations that were mentioned most often are the *The Times Top 100 Graduate Employers* for 2005.

It is clear from the considerable selection of answers given by finalists in the 'Class of 2005' that individual students used very different criteria to determine which employer they considered offered the best opportunities for graduates. Some focused on employers' general reputations – their public image, their business profile or their commercial success. Others evaluated employers based on the information they had seen during their job search – the quality of recruitment promotions, the impression formed

THE TIMES
TOP 100
GRADUATE EMPLOYERS

The Top 100 Graduate Employers 2005

This Year	Last Year		This Year	Last Year	
1.	1	PricewaterhouseCoopers	51.	57	Arcadia Group
2.	2	Civil Service	52.	59	John Lewis
3.	3	Accenture	53.	68	Oxfam
4.	4	KPMG	54.	47	Royal Navy
5.	6	BBC	55.	53	QinetiQ
6.	10	Deloitte	56.	51	Boots
7.	5	NHS	57.	56	Allen & Overy
8.	9	HSBC	58.	50	Reuters
9.	11	Goldman Sachs	59.	52	Freshfields Bruckhaus Deringer
10.	8	Procter & Gamble	60.	62	Cadbury Schweppes
11.	7	Army	61.	80	ExxonMobil
12.	12	Shell	62.	61	Baker & McKenzie
13.	19	GlaxoSmithKline	63.	76	HBOS
14.	14	Ernst & Young	64.	54	Pfizer
15.	15	Royal Bank of Scotland Group	65.	78	Airbus
16.	18	IBM	66.	94	Atkins
17.	16	JP Morgan	67.	69	Fast Track Teaching
18.	13	Unilever	68.	86	ABN Amro
19.	41	Teach First	69.	73	Mercer HR Consulting
20.	36	Police	70.	NEW	Penguin
21.	21	Microsoft	71.	66	Lovells
22.	23	Aldi	72.	63	MI5 – The Security Service
23.	35	Deutsche Bank	73.	71	Slaughter and May
24.	24	Rolls-Royce	74.	79	Cancer Research UK
25.	32	BP	75.	60	WPP
26.	30	L'Oréal	76.	82	DLA Piper Rudnick Gray Cary
27.	28	BAE Systems	77.	93	Lehman Brothers
28.	25	Barclays Bank	78.	58	Bain & Company
29.	44	Clifford Chance	79.	87	British Airways
30.	17	Marks & Spencer	80.	72	Herbert Smith
31.	42	Citigroup	81.	NEW	Saatchi & Saatchi
32.	40	RAF	82.	NEW	Corus
33.	46	NGDP for Local Government	83.	64	Ministry of Defence
34.	38	Lloyds TSB	84.	96	Barclays Capital
35.	34	Tesco	85.	NEW	Google
36.	27	Asda	86.	NEW	Data Connection
37.	20	Sainsbury's	87.	85	Boston Consulting Group
38.	39	McKinsey & Co	88.	NEW	Environment Agency
39.	29	Arup	89.	NEW	GCHQ
40.	22	BT	90.	95	British Nuclear Group
41.	43	Foreign & Commonwealth Office	91.	75	Ford
42.	26	Morgan Stanley	92.	NEW	PA Consulting
43.	49	Linklaters	93.	NEW	Bloomberg
44.	55	Eversheds	94.	88	Dstl
45.	33	AstraZeneca	95.	NEW	Simmons & Simmons
46.	37	Diageo	96.	91	Sony
47.	31	UBS	97.	NEW	ICI
48.	45	Mars	98.	NEW	Intel
49.	48	McDonald's Restaurants	99.	97	Siemens
50.	65	Merrill Lynch	100.	70	Credit Suisse First Boston

Source **The UK Graduate Careers Survey 2005**, High Fliers Research Ltd. 16,113 final year students leaving UK universities in the summer 2005 were asked 'Which employer do you think offers the best opportunities for graduates?'

from meeting employers' representatives, or experiences through the recruitment and selection process. Finalists also considered the numbers of vacancies that organisations were recruiting for as an indicator of graduates' prospects, or were influenced by an employer's profile on campus.

Many students, however, used the 'employment proposition' as their main guide – the quality of graduate training and development that an employer offers, the remuneration package available, and the practical aspects of a first job such as location or working hours.

Regardless of the criteria that students used to arrive at their answer, the hardest part for many was just selecting a single organisation. In many ways, choosing two or three, or even half a dozen employers would have been much easier. But the whole purpose of the exercise was to replicate the reality that everyone faces – you can only work for one organisation. And at each stage of the job search there are choices to be made as to which direction to take and which employers to pursue.

The resulting *Top 100* is a dynamic league table of the UK's most exciting and well-respected graduate recruiters in 2005. For the second year running, the accounting and professional services firm, Pricewaterhouse-Coopers has been rated the UK's top graduate recruiter. Just under 9 per cent of finalists voted for the firm, which is currently Britain's largest graduate recruiter. The Civil Service and consulting company Accenture, both former number ones in the *Top 100*, remain unchanged in 2nd and 3rd place this year. KPMG, the second most-popular 'Big Four' professional services firm is also a non-mover in 4th place.

Just behind them, the BBC has climbed one place to reach the top five for the first time. Deloitte, the next 'Big Four' firm has moved up four places to its highest-ever ranking. The NHS, after its three-year meteoric rise to number five has slipped back a little to 7th place in 2005. Banking group HSBC edges up to 8th place, just ahead of Goldman Sachs who return to 9th place after three years outside the top ten. Fast-moving consumer goods company, Procter & Gamble, moves down two to 10th place.

Elsewhere in the top twenty there have been a number of notable changes. The Army has dropped out of the top ten for the first time in seven years and is ranked in 11th place, its popularity inevitably effected by the on-going conflict in Iraq. GlaxoSmithKline has reached its highest-ever position of 13th place.

Two of the biggest risers in this year's *Top 100* are Teach First and the Police who have jumped twenty-two and sixteen places respectively to be ranked inside the top twenty. Two high climbers from 2004 did not continue their upward progress – The Royal Bank of Scotland Group is unchanged in 15th place and investment bank JP Morgan nudges down a place to 17th.

Several of the leading retailers have not fared at all well in this year's *Top 100*. Sainsbury's have dropped seventeen places to 37th, Marks & Spencer are down thirteen to 30th place, whilst rivals Tesco and Asda are lower too. This means that Aldi is the highest-ranking retail employer for 2005, in 22nd place.

Other major falls in this year's *Top 100* include BT which moves down eighteen places to 40th position, the Ministry of Defence drops a further nineteen to 83rd place, and the motor manufacturer Ford – a former top twenty employer – which has slid again, this time to 91st place. After big drops in 2004, ExxonMobil and British Airways have both moved back up the table this year.

Investment banks enjoyed mixed fortunes in the 2005 league table – Deutsche Bank, Citigroup, Merrill Lynch and ABN Amro each improved their rankings, but both UBS and Morgan Stanley fell out of the top forty. The Local Government's national graduate development scheme (NGDP), one of the highest new entries in 2003 continues to make good progress and has climbed to 33rd place.

Despite final year students' enthusiasm for charity and voluntary work – almost one in ten finalists applied for jobs in the sector – just two major charities, Oxfam and Cancer Research UK are ranked amongst this year's top employers.

There are a total of twelve new entries in the new *Top 100*, the highest being book-publishing group Penguin in 70th place. Advertising group Saatchi and Saatchi have appeared in 81st place, just ahead of steel-maker Corus in 82nd place and the first 'dot-com' company to be ranked in the *Top 100*, Google in 85th position. Other new entries include the Environment

Agency and information group Bloomberg. ICI, a former top-five employer in 1997, returns to the *Top 100* in 97th place.

Among the companies leaving the league table in 2005 were consumer-goods company Nestlé, mobile phone giants Vodafone and Orange, Scottish finance company Standard Life, accounting firm BDO Stoy Hayward, the long-standing student favourite Virgin, and the European Commission.

In the nine years since the first edition of the league table of top employers was produced, there have been just four organisations at number one – Marks & Spencer in 1997, Accenture (formerly Andersen Consulting) for five consecutive years 1998-2002, the Civil Service in 2003, and now Pricewaterhouse-Coopers in 2004 and 2005.

This year's edition of *The Times Top 100 Graduate Employers* provides an unique insight into how graduates from the 'Class of 2005' rated the leading employers. Many of these organisations are featured in the 'Employer Entry' section of this book. Starting on page 39, you can see a two-page profile for each employer, listed alphabetically for easy reference.

The editorial part of the entry includes a short description of what the organisation does, its opportunities for graduates and its recruitment programme for 2005-2006. A fact file for each employer gives details of the number of graduate vacancies, the business functions that graduates are recruited for, likely starting salaries for 2006, application deadlines, the universities that the employer is intending to visit during the year, and contact details for their recruitment website and graduate brochure. The right-hand page of the entry contains a display advert from the employer.

If you would like to find out more about any of the employers featured in *The Times Top 100 Graduate Employers*, then you can use the book's 'Information Request Service' – simply register your personal details and the employers you are interested in using the request card that appears opposite page 192, or go online to **www.Top100GraduateEmployers.com**.

You'll receive email bulletins about the employers, details of their presentations and careers events at your university, and other information about their graduate recruitment. The service is entirely free and you choose which organisations you would like to hear about.

Using the 'Information Request Service' enters you into a prize draw to win **£5,000**. There are also 50 **iPod Shuffles** to be won – one at each of the universities at which the *Top 100* book is distributed, for those who return their information request cards before **30th November 2005**.

THE TIMES TOP 100 GRADUATE EMPLOYERS

Employers in this year's Top 100

		Number of Employers				Number of Employers
1.	**Public Sector Employer**	15	9.	**Media Company**		6
2.	**Investment Bank**	11	10.	**Bank or Financial Institution**		5
3.	**Law Firm**	11	11.	**Accountancy or Professional Services Firm**		4
4.	**Engineering or Industrial Company**	10	12.	**Chemical or Pharmaceutical Company**		4
5.	**Retailer**	9	13.	**Oil Company**		3
6.	**Consulting Firm**	6	14.	**Charity or Voluntary Sector**		2
7.	**Fast-Moving Consumer Goods Company**	6	15.	**Motor Manufacturer**		1
8.	**IT or Telecoms Company**	6	16.	**Other**		1

Source **The UK Graduate Careers Survey 2005**, High Fliers Research Ltd. 16,113 final year students leaving UK universities in the summer 2005 were asked 'Which employer do you think offers the best opportunities for graduates?'

far-reaching

5-year Finance Leader Development Programme

At BAE Systems, we offer a unique, five-year finance training scheme – which means you can look beyond CIMA qualification and set your sights on a senior finance leadership role.

We are a leader in the development, delivery and support of state-of-the-art defence and aerospace systems. As we work to develop the next generation of intelligent systems, our Finance function is key to optimising business performance, which is why we need to equip talented and motivated graduates with all-round financial, leadership and business expertise.

We are a 'CIMA Training – Quality Partner', so you'll be joining a highly regarded programme. This will mean working on real projects and having all the tools you need to perform at your best up to and beyond CIMA qualification. But to thrive in our demanding environment, you will need to be resilient, analytical and practical – someone who can embrace our hands-on approach to finance.

To find out more about our Finance Leader Development Programme (FLDP) and our academic requirements, and to apply online, go to www.graduates-baesystems.com

BAE Systems' technology sits at the heart of the F-35 Joint Strike Fighter, the largest defence programme in the world

BAE SYSTEMS

THE TIMES
TOP 100
GRADUATE EMPLOYERS

How to use the directory

Many of the employers listed within *The Times Top 100 Graduate Employers* are featured in the 'Employer Entries' section of the directory. These entries describe what each organisation does, the opportunities they offer graduates, and practical details about their recruitment programme for 2005-2006.

The 'Employer Entry' section begins on page 39.

Each entry follows a standard format, and contains two elements: descriptive text and easy-to-find information on the employer's vacancies, contact details and salary expectations.

Locations of jobs
The regional locations of the employer's jobs are highlighted in red.

Vacancies
The number of likely graduate vacancies at this employer in 2005-2006.

Employer's graduate recruitment website

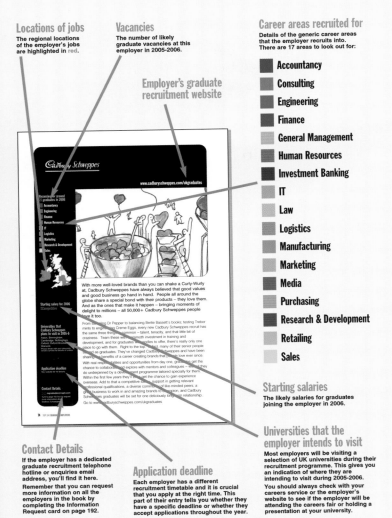

Career areas recruited for
Details of the generic career areas that the employer recruits into. There are 17 areas to look out for:

- Accountancy
- Consulting
- Engineering
- Finance
- General Management
- Human Resources
- Investment Banking
- IT
- Law
- Logistics
- Manufacturing
- Marketing
- Media
- Purchasing
- Research & Development
- Retailing
- Sales

Starting salaries
The likely salaries for graduates joining the employer in 2006.

Universities that the employer intends to visit
Most employers will be visiting a selection of UK universities during their recruitment programme. This gives you an indication of where they are intending to visit during 2005-2006.
You should always check with your careers service or the employer's website to see if the employer will be attending the careers fair or holding a presentation at your university.

Contact Details
If the employer has a dedicated graduate recruitment telephone hotline or enquiries email address, you'll find it here.
Remember that you can request more information on all the employers in the book by completing the Information Request card on page 192.

Application deadline
Each employer has a different recruitment timetable and it is crucial that you apply at the right time. This part of their entry tells you whether they have a specific deadline or whether they accept applications throughout the year.

BARCLAYS

It is why you stick
when other people twist.

But there's more to It than just a work hard, play hard mentality. It is about energy. It is about ambition. It is about jumping in with both feet. It is what makes you eager to learn about the world of financial services, and develop your career with a leading FTSE 100 company. It is why you deserve the very best training and development. And It is also why you deserve a higher salary than most. In short, It is the indefinable quality which separates a good graduate from a potential business leader. And It is what we look for here at Barclays. Not everybody has It, but if you think you do, visit www.barclays.co.uk/careers

Have you got It?
The business leadership programme

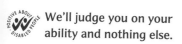 **We'll judge you on your ability and nothing else.**

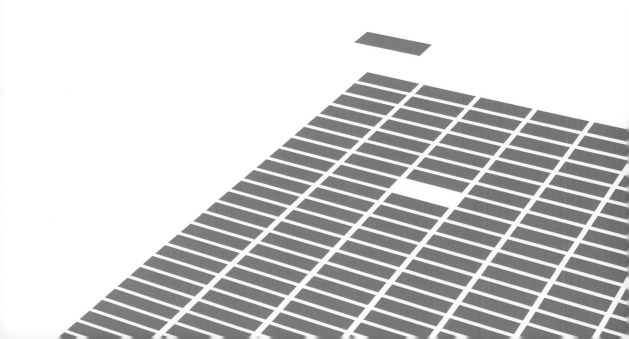

The

world

The Mars Management Development Programme is business training and
then some. It's unashamedly exclusive for stars-in-the-making. Our galaxy
of past 'graduates' includes CEOs, Chairmen, company Presidents and
even a Lord. Visit www.mars.com/ultimategrads for more. A lot more.

is

not

enough.

The ultimate business school

Understanding the Graduate Market

by Alison Hodgson
Chair, Association of Graduate Recruiters

For the second year running, there is some excellent news for job hunters from the latest survey of graduate salaries and vacancies from the Association of Graduate Recruiters (AGR).

The AGR Graduate Recruitment Survey 2005, produced during the summer of 2005 by High Fliers Research was based on information from more than 200 of Britain's best-known graduate employers and shows the employment market for university-leavers has been extremely buoyant in 2004-2005.

The survey shows that for the second consecutive year, there has been a significant rise in the number of graduate vacancies on offer during the 2005 recruitment season, compared with recruitment levels in 2004. The total number of graduate-level jobs on offer in 2005 at the 224 AGR employers who took part in the survey was 16,900, up 11.3 per cent on the 15,179 graduates recruited by the same organisations in 2004.

Recruitment levels have now gone up by more than quarter since 2003 and have risen four times in the last six recruitment seasons. In 2005, a total of 55 per cent of employers reported that their vacancies had increased and nearly half of these hired at least 10 extra graduates. Fifteen organisations reported expanding their graduate intake by at least 50 places, including each of the 'Big Four' accounting and professional services firms, three IT companies, two consulting firms,

three major banks, two public-sector recruiters and a leading retail group. The largest single increase was more than 200 extra vacancies at an accountancy firm, which increased its graduate intake by a third, year-on-year. Not every employer extended their graduate programme during 2004-2005, though, and recruitment levels at a sixth of employers were unchanged from 2004, with just over a quarter reducing their intake.

The final vacancy numbers for 2005 show that there is a very wide variation in the scale of recruitment undertaken by employers. Almost half had 25 or fewer vacancies and some thirty recruiters reported hiring less than 10 graduates this year. By contrast, twelve employers recruited at least 250 graduates, with six of these taking on 500 or more. For the first time in a number of years, two employers – both major professional services firms – reported that they were recruiting more than 1,000 new graduates to start work around the UK this autumn. The average vacancy level for AGR members in 2005 was 29 positions per organisation.

Looking at the number of graduate positions in different industries, the survey shows that almost a quarter of all vacancies amongst AGR employers were at accountancy or professional services firms and over three-quarters of these, nearly 3,500 in total, were with the 'Big Four' firms – PricewaterhouseCoopers, Deloitte, KPMG

JUST WHAT IS THE ACA
AND WHERE EXACTLY
CAN IT TAKE YOU?

THE ACA IS *THE* BUSINESS QUALIFICATION FOR PEOPLE WHO WANT
EXCEPTIONAL REWARDS, CAREER CHOICE AND THE CHALLENGES THAT
COME FROM WORKING AT THE HIGHEST LEVELS OF BUSINESS. WITH THE
PRESTIGE OF THE ACA QUALIFICATION BEHIND YOU, YOUR REPUTATION
WILL PRECEDE YOU.

AS AN ACA QUALIFIED CHARTERED ACCOUNTANT, YOU'LL EMBARK
ON A CAREER OF LIMITLESS POSSIBILITIES. IT WILL GIVE YOU THE ABILITY
TO WORK WITH PRETTY MUCH ANY EMPLOYER, OF ANY SIZE AND IN ANY
SECTOR YOU CHOOSE – IN BUSINESS, COMMERCE, THE PUBLIC SECTOR
OR EVEN AT THE HEAD OF YOUR OWN VENTURE.

SO, WHERE EXACTLY CAN IT TAKE YOU? WELL, WHERE EXACTLY DO YOU
WANT TO GO?

TO GET ALL THE FACTS ABOUT THE ACA AND DISCOVER MORE ABOUT
THE OPPORTUNITIES AVAILABLE, VISIT: **WWW.ICAEW.CO.UK/CAREERS**

ACA
THE
BUSINESS
QUALIFICATION

GET THE FACTS.
DISCOVER THE
OPPORTUNITIES.

and Ernst & Young. The next largest recruiters were the investment banks and fund managers, engineering and industrial companies, the public sector and law firms. Together, these five employment areas accounted for nearly two-thirds of vacancies recorded in the survey. The lowest numbers of positions were at transport and logistics companies, motor manufacturers, hotel and catering groups, and media companies – which together offered less than 2 per cent of the total graduate jobs available in 2005.

The substantial rise in total graduate vacancies between 2004 and 2005 means that recruitment did increase in most individual business areas and industries. In all, twelve different types of employer recorded increases in vacancy levels including IT companies, construction firms and accountancy or professional-services firms – each recruited at least a fifth more graduates.

Geographically, almost half the vacancies for graduates at AGR employers in 2005 were in London and a further tenth were elsewhere in the south east of England. This meant that the number of graduate positions available in other parts of the UK or beyond remains low. The next largest recruiting regions were the Midlands (7.7%) and the north west of England (6.3%). Graduate recruitment in Scotland, Wales and Northern Ireland amounted to less than 7% of the total graduate vacancies.

By business function or job type, graduate recruitment in 2005 was dominated by chartered accountancy, general management and engineering positions, which amounted to nearly half the total jobs available. Marketing, one of the most popular career choices for university-leavers, had less than 200 vacancies for the whole of the UK in 2005.

The AGR Graduate Recruitment Survey 2005 also examined the starting salaries on offer from Britain's leading graduate employers. There is good news here too because the survey shows that remuneration packages on offer to new graduates starting work in 2005 rose to record levels. Employers were offering an average salary of £22,000 to those starting work in autumn 2005 – £1,000 more than the £21,000 average starting salary paid in 2004.

This year-on-year increase of 4.8 per cent is well above the 3.4 per cent rise recorded in 2004 and is the third consecutive year that salaries have risen by considerably more than a 'cost-of-living' increase (currently taken to be between 2 and 2.5 per cent, based on the government's inflation targets). In the five years since 2001, graduate starting salaries have risen by 15.8 per

THE TIMES

TOP 100
GRADUATE EMPLOYERS

TOP 100 GRADUATE EMP
TOP 100 GRADUATE EM
TOP 100 GRADUATE EM
TOP 100 GRADUATE EM
TOP 100 GRADUATE EMP
TOP 100 GRADUATE EM
TOP 100 GRADUATE EM
TOP 100 GRADUATE EM
TOP 100 GRADUATE EN
TOP 100 GRADUATE EN

Graduate Employment 2005, by Industry

		% of total vacancies in 2005	How vacancy numbers changed since 2004	Average starting salaries for new graduates in 2005
1.	**Accountancy/Professional Services**	24.3	Up 20.4%	£22,000
2.	**Investment Bank/Fund Manager**	11.7	Up 16.7%	£35,000
3.	**Engineering/Industrial Company**	8.8	Up 2.6%	£20,800
4.	**Public Sector**	8.3	Up 6.6%	£22,000
5.	**Law Firm**	8.0	No change	£28,000
6.	**Consulting Firm**	6.4	Up 16.8%	£28,500
7.	**Retailer**	6.2	Up 9.4%	£20,000
8.	**Armed Forces**	5.3	Down 4.1%	£25,600
9.	**Banking/Financial Services**	4.9	Up 11.9%	£23,000
10.	**IT Hardware/Software Company**	4.4	Up 46.5%	£22,000
11.	**Construction Company**	1.9	Up 24.6%	£20,600
12.	**Telecommunications Company**	1.6	No change	£21,500
13.	**FMCG Company**	1.4	Up 6.0%	£24,500
14.	**Oil Company**	1.3	Down 2.7%	£27,000
15.	**Energy/Water/Utility Company**	1.2	Down 13.6%	£22,000

Source **The AGR Graduate Recruitment Survey 2005**, High Fliers Research Ltd. 224 graduate employers were asked about their vacancy levels and starting salaries for graduates beginning work with their organisations in autumn 2005.

cent, by comparison to the estimated 9.3 per cent increased cost of living over the same period.

Starting salaries offered by employers in 2005 did vary considerably from organisation to organisation. Only two recruiters offered new graduates £15,000 or less in 2005 and a further nine advertised salaries up to £17,500. At the top of the market, more than a quarter of all recruiters expect their 2005 recruits to start on £25,000 or more – approximately 5,800 graduate positions. A record sixteen employers, mainly from the investment banking, consulting and legal sectors, who together recruited over 1,700 graduates in 2005, planned to pay their new graduates at least £35,000. Two recruiters declared starting salaries of £40,000 for 2005.

Reviewing salaries by industry shows that the highest-paying employers in 2005 were once again the investment banks or fund managers, consulting firms and law firms. All three sectors have paid top starting salaries of between £28,000 and £35,000 for the last three years, but each of the sectors' median rates have remained unchanged since at least 2002. Six other business sectors paid salaries above the national average of £22,000, with oil companies and the Armed Forces offering the most generous packages. The lowest salaries were for those

starting work at insurance companies, hotel or catering groups, media companies and retailers, where the median salaries were £20,000 or less.

By region, there were very substantial differences in the rates of pay for new graduates in 2005. Graduates employed in London undoubtedly achieved the highest rates – a median of £26,500, although this does include any London weighting or allowances that employers provided. The south east of England is the only other region where salaries matched the national average. In all other parts of the UK graduates could expect lesser packages, with the lowest salaries in Northern Ireland and Wales.

Analysed by business function or job type, the highest graduate starting salaries in 2005 were for positions in investment banking, consulting, legal work, general management, and financial management – new graduates could expect salaries of between £25,000 and £35,000 in each area. The lowest rates were for jobs in sales, retail management, logistics, surveying and engineering.

Although much of the news about graduate salaries and vacancies is extremely positive, it is worth remembering that competition for these top jobs remains intense. The survey shows that application levels for graduate jobs remained

THE TIMES TOP 100 GRADUATE EMPLOYERS

Graduate Employment 2005, by Job Type

		% of total vacancies in 2005	How vacancy numbers changed since 2004	Average starting salaries for new graduates in 2005
1.	Chartered Accountancy	23.1	Up 15.6%	£22,000
2.	General Management	15.4	Up 3.9%	£25,500
3.	Investment Banking	8.8	Up 15.7%	£35,000
4.	Legal Work	8.1	Down 2.6%	£28,000
5.	IT	7.1	Up 32.8%	£22,000
6.	Consulting	6.7	Up 26.9%	£28,500
7.	Retail Management	5.1	Up 25.5%	£20,300
8.	Civil Engineering	3.3	Up 18.2%	£20,000
9.	Electrical/Electronic Engineering	2.5	Up 1.0%	£20,800
10.	Financial Management	2.4	Up 16.0%	£25,000
11.	Sales	2.4	Down 2.9%	£19,500
12.	Mechanical Engineering	2.3	Up 7.9%	£21,000
13.	Science, Research & Development	1.8	Down 18.9%	£21,000
14.	Manufacturing Engineering	1.5	Up 7.4%	£21,800
15.	Purchasing	1.3	Up 8.0%	£21,100

Source **The AGR Graduate Recruitment Survey 2005**, High Fliers Research Ltd. 224 graduate employers were asked about their vacancy levels and starting salaries for graduates beginning work with their organisations in autumn 2005.

high in 2004-2005 and recruiters received an average of 32.9 applications per vacancy.

There were differing application levels between organisations – half received fewer than 1,000 applications as a result of their recruitment campaign in 2004-2005, and yet six individual recruiters attracted upwards of 10,000 applications from candidates. Some 40 per cent of employers received between 1,000 and 5,000 applications, the average for the recruitment season being 2,490 applicants per organisation. Examining application levels by industry or

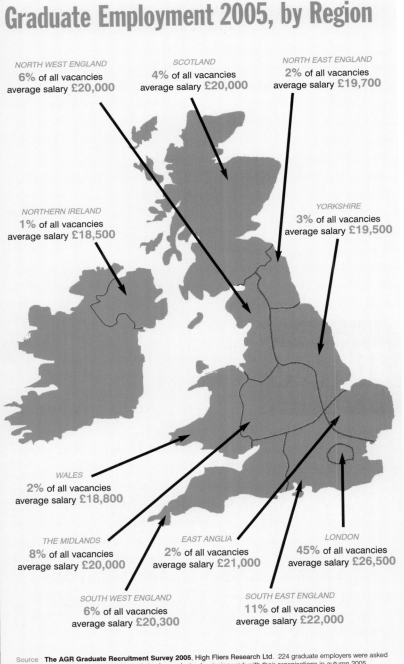

Graduate Employment 2005, by Region

NORTH WEST ENGLAND
6% of all vacancies
average salary £20,000

SCOTLAND
4% of all vacancies
average salary £20,000

NORTH EAST ENGLAND
2% of all vacancies
average salary £19,700

NORTHERN IRELAND
1% of all vacancies
average salary £18,500

YORKSHIRE
3% of all vacancies
average salary £19,500

WALES
2% of all vacancies
average salary £18,800

THE MIDLANDS
8% of all vacancies
average salary £20,000

EAST ANGLIA
2% of all vacancies
average salary £21,000

LONDON
45% of all vacancies
average salary £26,500

SOUTH WEST ENGLAND
6% of all vacancies
average salary £20,300

SOUTH EAST ENGLAND
11% of all vacancies
average salary £22,000

Source **The AGR Graduate Recruitment Survey 2005**, High Fliers Research Ltd. 224 graduate employers were asked about their vacancy levels and starting salaries for graduates beginning work with their organisations in autumn 2005.

Could you turn your potential into performance?

The High Potential Development (HPD) scheme has been designed to support and develop the future leaders of the Police service, to improve their leadership and command skills, and assist them to progress to senior positions.

The scheme encourages individuals to fulfil their own expectations, pursue specific areas of interest and broaden their horizons. The greater the effort, commitment and initiative of the applicant, the greater the prospective rewards.

The High Potential Development scheme
Exceptional opportunities for exceptional graduates

To go forward, call 020 7035 5050
or visit www.policecouldyou.co.uk

business sector, fast-moving consumer goods companies – often synonymous with opportunities in marketing – received the highest average number of applications, over 120 per vacancy. Other popular employers include chemical or pharmaceutical companies, telecommunications companies and oil companies, each of which attracted at least 60 applications per graduate job. The lowest application rate was for the accountancy or professional-services firms, an average of just 16 applications per job.

The survey also revealed the success rates for candidates applying for graduate positions in 2004-2005. Of the average 32.9 candidates who applied for each vacancy, 5.7 were invited to a first-round interview, and 2.5 went on to final assessment centres.

During the 2004-2005 recruitment season, employers used a number of different selection criteria to assess applicants for their graduate programmes. The most commonly stipulated 'minimum criteria' for applicants were specific academic results – two-thirds of all recruiters insisted on 2.1 degrees or above and a further quarter wanted their applicants to attain at least a 2.2 degree. 'A' level results were another popular indicator and 37% of employers had advertised a minimum UCAS tariff. The most common requirement was for the equivalent of 'BBB' at 'A' level, but a quarter expected a higher standard.

The vast majority of recruiters accepted applications via their website during 2004-2005,

but 44 per cent of employers were still happy to accept paper-based applications or CVs with a covering letter. Most employers used the three-stage recruitment process of 'application, first interview, assessment centre' for their graduate recruitment. At least a third of employers used an online self-selection or pre-qualification exercise to try and discourage casual applicants.

Employers' outlook for 2005-2006 is very encouraging, with more than a quarter of recruiters anticipating expanding their intake next year and around half expecting to maintain the increased recruitment levels achieved in 2005. Less than one in fourteen employers thought that their graduate programmes would be scaled back in 2006.

Salary prospects for graduates in the 'Class of 2006' are bright too as the majority of employers, nearly three-quarters of recruiters questioned, believed that 2006 salary levels would be likely to increase by the cost of living or more.

Looking back at recruiters' recent predictions makes interesting reading. In 2003, 52 per cent of employers thought their salaries would increase during the following recruitment season – the resulting rise in salaries in 2004 was 3.4 per cent year-on-year. In the 2004 survey, 67 per cent of employers believed their salaries would rise – the actual annual increase in salaries in 2005 has been 4.8 per cent. If this trend to continues, it would suggest that graduate salaries are set to rise sharply again in 2006.

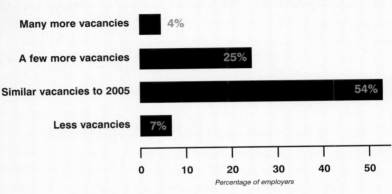

Outlook for Graduate Vacancies in 2006

Many more vacancies	4%
A few more vacancies	25%
Similar vacancies to 2005	54%
Less vacancies	7%

Percentage of employers

Source **The AGR Graduate Recruitment Survey 2005**, High Fliers Research Ltd. 224 graduate employers were asked about their vacancy levels and starting salaries for graduates beginning work with their organisations in autumn 2005.

Deadline for applications is December 9th.

A date for your diary, calendar, fridge door, mobile, bathroom mirror and post-it notes strategically arranged around the house.

Successful Job Hunting

by Martin Thorne
Director, Centre for Career Development
University of Nottingham

It may seem a daunting prospect, but sooner or later your time at university will inevitably come to an end and life as a graduate will begin. Deciding what to do next and finding rewarding employment can be just as challenging as securing a good degree but an excellent first step is to get to know some of the job-hunting resources that are available on your doorstep.

Every university in the UK has its own careers service, provided and funded by the institution, which offer a wealth of information and guidance about the alternatives for university-leavers. At the start of the autumn term, many careers services run introductory briefing sessions or tours which can give an overview of their facilities and may also be a very useful way to 'break the ice' at the start of your job search.

Some people are understandably reluctant to come forward because they don't know what they want to do, but that's exactly what the careers services are there to help with. It's natural to feel slightly embarrassed about things, but there is much you can do in terms of researching your options, talking to careers service staff and making contact with recent graduates that can help you begin forming your ideas. This initial visit to your careers service can also provide information about the workshops, seminars and courses taking place at your university explaining the different stages in the recruitment process.

Most careers services now have extensive websites that provide a virtual careers resource and you can get a good overview of the facilities that exist and the processes that the careers service can help with, just by spending half an hour exploring the website, something which could be done at anytime of the day or night.

Every careers service has a team of careers advisers who offer first hand advice on job hunting. Most universities now provide a mixture of fairly short but instantly available consultations, along with more reflective in-depth counselling which normally needs to be booked in advance. The 'drop-in' sessions can be useful to get pointers or encouragement about specific aspects of a job search or for an immediate answer to an enquiry. For example, there are often rumours about employer's closing dates or application requirements – fifteen minutes with a careers adviser can sort out fact from fiction.

The longer in-depth appointments typically last up to an hour and there is therefore much more opportunity for the adviser to get to know you and understand your interests, motivations and aspirations. However, at the busiest times of the year, because of the demand for careers advisers these longer sessions may not be available or can have a two or three-week waiting list.

It's important to understand what careers advisers can offer in terms of guidance. Advisers do not see it as their job to tell people what to do

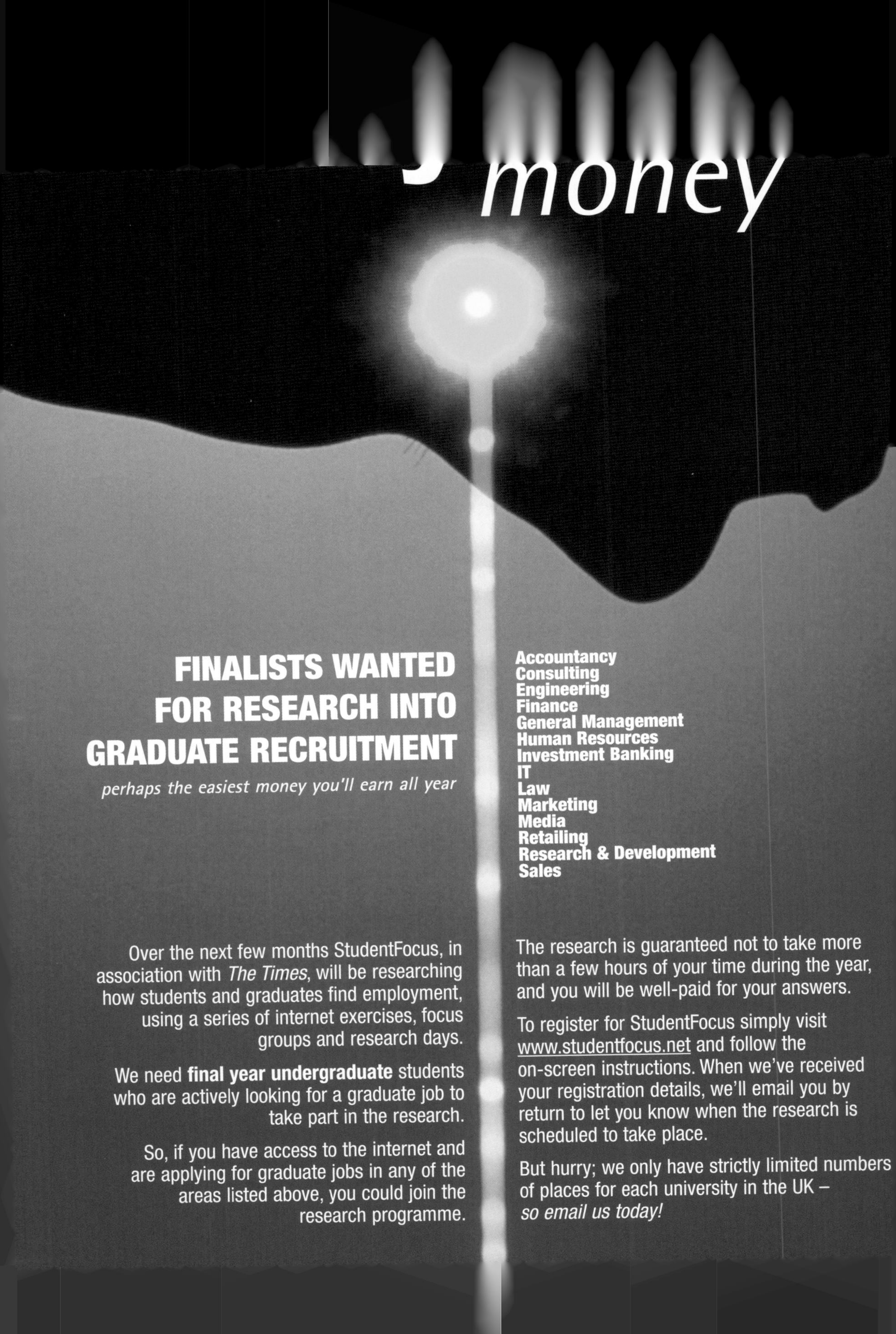

money

FINALISTS WANTED FOR RESEARCH INTO GRADUATE RECRUITMENT

perhaps the easiest money you'll earn all year

Accountancy
Consulting
Engineering
Finance
General Management
Human Resources
Investment Banking
IT
Law
Marketing
Media
Retailing
Research & Development
Sales

Over the next few months StudentFocus, in association with *The Times*, will be researching how students and graduates find employment, using a series of internet exercises, focus groups and research days.

We need **final year undergraduate** students who are actively looking for a graduate job to take part in the research.

So, if you have access to the internet and are applying for graduate jobs in any of the areas listed above, you could join the research programme.

The research is guaranteed not to take more than a few hours of your time during the year, and you will be well-paid for your answers.

To register for StudentFocus simply visit www.studentfocus.net and follow the on-screen instructions. When we've received your registration details, we'll email you by return to let you know when the research is scheduled to take place.

But hurry; we only have strictly limited numbers of places for each university in the UK – *so email us today!*

with their lives and what to do after graduation. They will not direct you to a particular career path or tell you what is the right or best career to follow – that is a subjective and value judgement for which you need to take responsibility yourself. The role of an adviser is to help and support you to make your own choices and decisions and to guide you towards the information that you need. Because they're working within your university, advisers will be familiar with your course and the kind of things that previous graduates have done. Many advisers specialise in particular degree courses although some may concentrate on certain occupational areas too. All consultations are entirely confidential and individual students are never discussed with employers without your prior knowledge and consent.

The majority of students try to work out what type of jobs they are interested in before pinpointing which industries or individual employers they are drawn to. There are a wide variety of handouts, careers guides and publications available from your careers service which can help explain different occupations, professions and employment areas. Their website is also likely to be signposted for information on occupational areas, including links to external websites such as relevant institutes and professional bodies.

One important detail to establish at this stage is whether you're eligible to work in the areas that you are considering. Over half of graduate jobs in the UK are for 'any degree' but it's useful to check the basic academic requirements of employers in the areas you are hoping to join.

As you start to narrow down the occupation types that you are interested in, talking to people who work in those areas can make a real difference and your careers service will usually be able to offer suggestions about who you could contact. They often have listings or databases of alumni who have gone into particular professions or fields of work and have volunteered themselves as contact points for current students or the careers service might have a tie-in with the alumni office. These contacts are very keen to help students from their own university, thinking of following in their footsteps, and are happy to respond to questions by email or sometimes offer a mobile phone number. It can give you a personal experience of how things have worked

out for previous graduates and in some cases, it may well be possible for alumni to arrange for students to visit their place of work. They usually have no direct involvement with the recruitment process and can therefore give more of a 'warts and all' account of their working experiences. It can also be helpful if, for example, you are hoping to work abroad, to get in touch with alumni working in the countries that interest you.

Careers services provide a very active range of events that can help you understand more about the type of employment that is available and the opportunities at specific organisations. At the larger universities, it isn't unusual to find a programme of 150-200 events. These include individual employer talks and presentations, where the employer sends representatives to talk to interested students, very often in the evening, outside of lecture times. Careers services will try and supplement these presentations with other events that include topics and working areas not covered by the major employers, using either an alumni speaker or a professional contact.

There are also the major careers fairs and exhibitions that take place during the autumn term and offer the chance to meet a large number of employers at a single event. These are sometimes organised by the careers service direct, with the Student Industrial Society, or through the campus branch of AIESEC, the international student society.

Many careers services also offer short courses of skills training, delivered either by careers service personnel, external trainers or employers. There may be programmes about employability skills, such as team working, communication and time management. Some careers services also run introductory courses on setting up your own business that are becoming increasingly popular.

To help you find out more about individual employers, there are several different resources available. There are a number of major directories and careers guides which your careers service will stock that can be very useful references to keep throughout the application process. There are also certain employers who produce paper brochures, although not every careers service still stocks them. The proportion of employers who provide their own brochure is undoubtedly decreasing because many organisations now rely on their websites to provide much of their information on career opportunities. A good starting point for employer websites may be the careers service's own site which often has links to individual organisations, often arranged by sector or job type.

The next thing to check is the vacancy information. At a large university which includes the full range of academic subjects, it's not unusual for the careers service to receive notifications of vacancies from 2,000 to 3,000 employers each year. Vacancies arise from all manner of employers – local, regional, national and international – and at all times of the year. Most careers services now have a large portion of their websites devoted to vacancy information and this is updated constantly, often on a daily basis. This resource is particularly useful because many of the vacancies are at employers which will not be instantly familiar. Whilst some graduates are successful in finding employment with a well-known name, not everybody is looking for that kind of opportunity. There is a very wide range of opportunities on offer from organisations that are either not large enough to be very well known or are not a consumer brand. Many of these employers are, however, represented among the careers service vacancy listings and can be searched by job type, location of work and industry.

There is no magic number in terms of the volume of applications that you need to make in order to secure your first graduate job. Some students are able to manage a very large number of applications without compromising their studies, yet others find even a few quite a struggle. Quality is always more important than quantity and if that means you end up making fewer applications but they are carefully researched, well articulated and clearly present your strengths then you are more likely to be successful. Remember too, there will always be a tomorrow as far as job applications go – if you don't manage to get what you're looking for first time round, there will be other chances later on.

In terms of preparation, most careers services will have handouts or online advice to help you put together a CV, with examples of different styles and ways to present your information. Be aware that many employers operate their own online application systems and no longer accept CVs, but the process of collecting together your relevant qualifications, skills and experiences is still essential; albeit without spending time producing a highly polished CV.

It's unfortunate that there are almost as many different application systems as there are employers recruiting graduates but the underlying questions that are being asked are often very similar – 'why are you interested in this kind of work?', 'why are you interested in this particular organisation?' and 'why should we be interested in you?'. A considerable part of the selection process is competency based, so employers will be asking candidates to present evidence from their own experience about how well they satisfy these competency requirements. You may well have completed a progress file or learning log during your time at university and these can be a good way to capture and record the different experiences and what you've learnt

THE TIMES TOP 100 GRADUATE EMPLOYERS

Type of Organisations the 'Class of 2005' Graduates Wanted to Join after University

		% of finalists
1.	Major National or International Company	46
2.	Small or Medium Sized Firms	18
3.	Government or Public Sector Employer	16
4.	Artistic, Charity or Voluntary Organisation	8
5.	Academic Institution	7
6.	Own Business or Freelance Work	5

Source **The UK Graduate Careers Survey 2005**, High Fliers Research Ltd. 16,113 final year students leaving who left UK universities in the summer of 2005 were asked which type of employer they were hoping to work for as a graduate.

STARE AT THE DOT FOR ABOUT ONE MINUTE
THEN TURN OVER QUICKLY AND LOOK AT
THE DOT IN THE CIRCLE...

from your university life, extracurricular activities and vacation work. If you have used one of these during your studies, it can be a very useful starting point when you are trying to demonstrate the competencies that you can offer.

The other thing that you are likely to face during selection is tests. These take various forms such as psychometric, numeracy or verbal reasoning and can be conducted online, either as part of the application process or later, or via testing sessions on campus or at their premises. Some careers services offer practice sessions which can give you an idea of the types of questions that employers use and experience what it feels like to answer questions against a stopwatch.

If your application is successful, you may well be invited for a first interview either on campus, at a regional centre or sometimes at an employer's head office. This is the traditional first stage in the main selection process before you reach the final round assessment centre and practice workshops or individual interview coaching may be available from your careers advisers. Similarly, with assessment centres many careers services run preparatory sessions to give you the chance to experience typical assessment centre exercises and get a feel for performing in a small group under observation from assessors.

Assessment centres often last for up to two days and will often take place at a residential training establishment or a hotel. They usually begin with a 'breaking the ice session', perhaps over a meal or drinks reception. There are likely to be small-group specific exercises such as discussions, problem-solving or case-studies where maybe four or five candidates work on a particular scenario, against a time deadline. It's an opportunity for the selectors to get a sense of how an individual operates within a team. There may also be a presentation exercise and almost certainly one or more individual interviews, plus more aptitude testing. It's important to remember that every part of the event contributes to your final assessment so it's essential to remain focused. The nice meal and free bar may seem quite attractive but even the social aspects of these centres are being assessed and can make the difference between a job offer and rejection.

If you don't manage to secure the graduate job you were hoping for, all is not lost. Your careers adviser can help you reflect on why things have gone wrong. Nobody likes rejection, but if you have reached the later stages of the selection process, this can be very encouraging. If you don't find a job before you leave university, all is not lost – many employers recruit on a year-round basis and others are happy to recruit those who have already graduated, so making a further round of applications can be very successful.

As a recent graduate, you are likely to be able to use all the main careers service facilities for two or three years after you've finished your course, including the online vacancy information and access to careers advisers.

THE TIMES TOP 100 GRADUATE EMPLOYERS

Leading Destinations for 2005 Graduates

	% who wanted to work in sector		% who wanted to work in sector
1. Teaching	12.7	13. Human Resources	6.5
2. Media	12.7	13. General Management	5.9
3. Marketing	11.7	14. Sales	5.6
4. Investment Banking	10.8	15. IT	5.2
5. Research & Development	9.9	16. Finance	4.9
6. Civil Service	9.9	17. Retailing	4.1
7. Consulting	9.9	18. Police	3.6
8. Accountancy	9.3	19. Armed Forces	2.9
9. Charity or Voluntary Work	8.6	20. Buying or Purchasing	2.5
10. Engineering	8.1	21. Actuarial Work	1.7
11. Solicitor or Barrister	7.6	22. Transport or Logistics	1.6

Source **The UK Graduate Careers Survey 2005**, High Fliers Research Ltd. 16,113 final year students leaving who left UK universities in the summer of 2005 were asked which sectors they had applied to or planned to apply to for a graduate job.

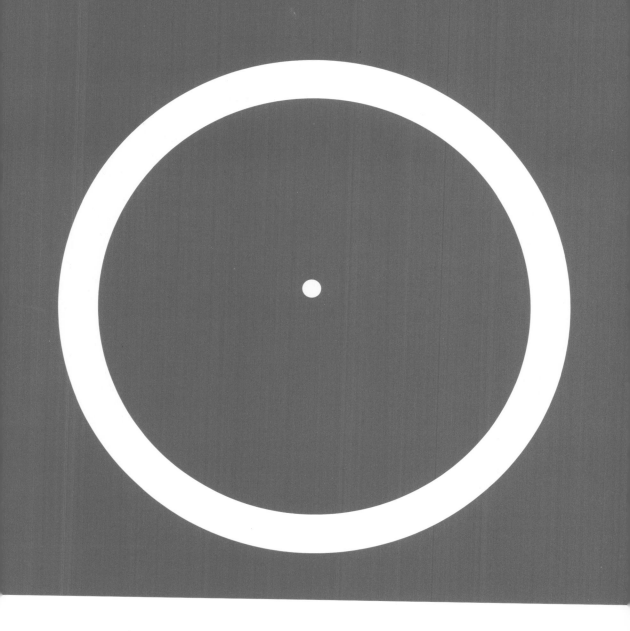

..THIS IS HOW LONG IT COULD TAKE TO PUT
YOURSELF IN THE PICTURE AT MILKROUND

FIND THE JOB OF YOU DREAMS

www.milkround.com

WHY CLIMB THE CAREER LADDER WHEN YOU CAN TAKE THE LIFT?

Get the only newspaper jobs section dedicated
to graduate to middle-management level positions.

CAREER, every Thursday in The Times.

THE TIMES
JOIN THE DEBATE

THE ⚜ TIMES

TOP 100

GRADUATE EMPLOYERS

www.graduate.abnamro.com

Vacancies for around 150 graduates in 2006

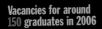

■ Finance
■ Investment Banking
■ IT

Vacancies also available throughout the world.

Starting salary for 2006
£Competitive

Universities ABN Amro plans to visit in 2005-6

Bath, Birmingham, Bristol, Cambridge, City, Edinburgh, London, Manchester, Nottingham, Oxford, Southampton, St Andrews, Warwick, York.
Please check with your university careers service for details of events.

Application deadline
11th November 2005
Please see website for full details.

Contact Details

 abnamrograd06@
alexmann.com

☎ 0870 351 3704

Turn to page 192 now to request more information about ABN Amro.

THE DEFINITIVE GUIDE TO CORPORATE AND INVESTMENT BANKING.

Alphabetically, ABN AMRO is top of the list. But if graduates are looking for a high-flying, rewarding career in business, they should be at the front of their mind as a graduate employer too.

ABN AMRO is one of the world's leading financial institutions with a global network in 59 countries. Their Wholesale Clients (WCS) business unit serves large corporations and institutions worldwide, giving them the benefit of local knowledge and world-class expertise.

Within the Graduate Development Programme, there are opportunities in Mergers & Acquisitions, Equities, Equity Capital Markets, Fixed Income, Derivatives, Portfolio Management, Finance and Accounting, Risk and Technology. For all business areas, the programme will start with six weeks of intensive training at the exclusive ABN AMRO Academy in Amsterdam. Blending industry simulations, technical instruction and business-specific training, this time will lay the foundations for a career with the bank. After that, graduates will join a development programme that gives a truly panoramic view of their chosen business area.

Throughout it all, graduates will be supported by the dedicated graduate development team, as well as a mentor and a buddy. At the same time, however, it's up to them to make the most of the opportunities that enable them to contribute to the business from day one.

As such, they need the ambition, tenacity, confidence and team spirit to act on ideas and build strong relationships with clients and colleagues alike. Academically, graduates must have 300 UCAS points and at least a 2.1 (or the overseas equivalents) in any discipline.

PREDICTING INFLATION*
COULD HELP YOU GO UP IN THE WORLD.

Global graduate careers

ABN AMRO is one of the world's leading financial institutions with a global network in 59 countries. We have opportunities for talented graduates in London, Amsterdam, New York, Hong Kong and Sydney. Our Graduate Development Programme starts with a six-week training course in Amsterdam, before enabling you to specialise in areas including mergers and acquisitions, equities and fixed income.

Raise your level of interest at www.graduate.abnamro.com

*Inflation – A percentage measure of the amount by which the prices of goods and services rise in the economy, over a period of time, usually one year.

High performance. Delivered.

accenture.com/ukgraduates

Vacancies for around 500-600 graduates in 2006

■ Consulting

■ IT

Starting salary for 2006
£28,500

Universities Accenture plans to visit in 2005-6

Bath, Birmingham, Bristol, Cambridge, Durham, Edinburgh, Glasgow, Leeds, Leicester, London, Loughborough, Manchester, Newcastle, Nottingham, Oxford, St Andrews, Strathclyde, Warwick.
Please check with your university careers service for details of events.

Application deadline
Year-round recruitment

Contact Details

✉ ukgraduates@accenture.com

Turn to page 192 now to request more information about Accenture.

With over 110,000 people working in 48 countries, Accenture is one of the world's leading management consulting, technology services and outsourcing organisations.

Accenture helps clients become high-performance businesses by delivering innovation and their work invariably involves the application of information technology to business challenges. They created a state-of-the-art showroom for Peugeot on the web; and helped transform Selfridges from a retailer with a single location to one with several centrally-managed sites.

There is a surprisingly close-knit feel to working at Accenture. Employees control their own development and promotion is based entirely on the skills acquired and the contribution made, while flexible working programmes allow for personal schedules.

They also actively encourage people to get involved in community and charitable activities that make a real difference to communities across the UK and around the world – from a day painting a refuge to six months transforming a business in the Balkans.

Graduates usually join as Analysts on their Analyst Training Programme. Accenture look for people with more than just excellent academics, who are passionate about something outside their studies, have some work experience and a strong interest in business and technology.

Accenture Technology Solutions is an alternative technology-focused career option for technologists who don't necessarily want to be consultants, and would prefer to build and maintain deep technical skills. For more information on this career path please visit www.accenturetechnologysolutions.com/uk.

Heads up.
High performers start here.

Go on. Be a Tiger.

Don't let the grass grow under your feet. If you're a high performer, we can offer you more opportunities to push your career forward than virtually anywhere else. We deliver international business and technology solutions for some of the most dynamic organisations around. Join our global team and you'll be delivering the innovation that helps our clients become high-performance businesses.

Graduate Careers in Consulting

Almost everything we do involves the application of IT to business challenges. But that's not to say you have to be a computer genius to get on here (although we certainly wouldn't hold it against you). If you're genuinely interested in business and technology, expect to achieve a 2:1 degree and have 24/300 UCAS points, we can offer you a truly rounded career.

As well as doing interesting and challenging work with exceptional people, and using the very latest technology, you'll be rewarded well with a salary of £28,500 and an additional £10,000 over your first two years.

We also actively encourage people to get involved in community and charitable activities that make a real difference to communities across the UK and around the world—from a day painting a refuge to six months transforming a business in the Balkans.

For people with the right intelligence and personal qualities, consulting is possibly the best job in the world. To find out more, and to apply, visit our website. Accenture is committed to being an equal opportunities employer.

Visit accenture.com/ukgraduates

Consulting • Technology • Outsourcing

> **accenture**
High performance. Delivered.

AIRBUS

www.airbus-careers.com

Vacancies for around 80 graduates in 2006

- Engineering
- Finance
- Human Resources
- IT
- Logistics
- Manufacturing
- Purchasing

Starting salary for 2006
£22,000

Universities that Airbus plans to visit in 2005-6
Bath, Bristol, Cambridge, London, Loughborough, Manchester, Nottingham, Southampton, Warwick.
Please check with your university careers service for details of events.

Application deadline
See website for full details.

Contact Details
Turn to page 192 now to request more information about Airbus.

Airbus is one of the world's leading aircraft manufacturers At the heart of their success are 53,000 people from 80 nationalities, who thrive on a mix of ideas, vision and knowledge. Combining their energy and drive Airbus has developed successive generations of aircraft that have pioneered new levels of technology, manufacturing and design. This innovative approach creates a variety of opportunities in a range of areas.

Free thinking and entrepreneurial graduates will enjoy the chance to develop individual talents and experience on the Airbus UK Direct Entry Graduate Scheme. The scheme provides the opportunity to develop in-depth knowledge of a business function through structured placements in the UK and, potentially, worldwide. The format is consistent but specific programmes depend on the function joined, experience, interests and current business challenges.

Airbus also provides access to excellent focused training and full support to achieve membership of professional institutions, further qualifications and long-term career planning. Involvement in education and community projects to broaden experience and skills is also actively encouraged.

Airbus UK in Filton, Bristol and Broughton, North Wales designs, supplies and supports the wings for all Airbus aircraft, including fuel systems and, in most cases, the landing gear.

Most opportunities are in design and manufacturing engineering, with further roles in procurement, human resources, finance, logistics, project management and information systems.

Know Airbus

Every four seconds an Airbus plane takes off or lands somewhere in the world.

and know how good you could be

As a global leader whose philosophy is built on listening and thinking creatively, Airbus gives you the freedom to turn innovative vision into reality.

Airbus UK Direct Entry Graduate Scheme

ENGINEERING

MANUFACTURING

FINANCE

PROCUREMENT

INFORMATION SYSTEMS

LOGISTICS

HUMAN RESOURCES

PROJECT MANAGEMENT

The twin-deck, 555-seater Airbus A380 is now the world's largest and most fuel efficient commercial airliner. Remarkable technological breakthroughs such as these are our hallmark at Airbus: a truly international organisation with a culture based on innovation, creativity and free-thinking.

We are now searching for ambitious and entrepreneurial graduates to join our specially designed Airbus UK Direct Entry Graduate Scheme. More specifically, we are looking for the following profiles:

• Qualifications in Engineering or appropriate degree

• Excellent individual performance

• Fluency in English

• Excellent communication and inter-personal skills

• Maximum 2 years professional experience

In return, we offer a programme of structured placements, development activities and focussed training programmes in a dynamic international business environment.

In addition, there is wide ranging support to gain professional qualifications, a competitive remuneration package, annual performance based reviews and outstanding long-term prospects.

For more information about the Airbus UK Direct Entry Graduate Scheme and details of September 2006 intake, please visit:

www.airbus-careers.com

Airbus. Setting the standards.

AIRBUS

ALDI

Vacancies for around 90 graduates in 2006

Retailing

Starting salary for 2006
£37,000
Plus Audi A4.

Universities that Aldi plans to visit in 2005-6
Please check with your university careers service for details of events.

Application deadline
Year-round recruitment

Contact Details
Turn to page 192 now to request more information about Aldi.

Aldi is one of the world's largest privately owned companies and, with over 6,000 stores worldwide is recognised as a world leader in grocery retailing. Pioneers in quality discount retailing, their unique culture and philosophy continue to promote exceptional standards of management and deliver unrivalled value for money for their customers.

The Area Management Programme offers superb opportunities for personal and career development to exceptional graduates who can prove they have drive and focus. An individual twelve month training plan quickly introduces trainees to the pace and excitement of retail operations, trading, logistics and property management. Starting in store and managing one within weeks, the programme progresses onto multi-site responsibilities, which offer graduates the broadest opportunities to develop their leadership style, commercial awareness and technical skills. As soon as Area Management graduates are ready, they'll be given a multi-million pound area of four to six stores to run as if they owned it.

Two year secondments to Europe or the USA are a real possibility. Within five years there's every chance of a directorship reporting to the Managing Director of a region, or the Group Buying Director.

Find out more by visiting www.aldi.com and apply online. Alternatively, send a CV and a recent photograph, quoting: Times 100, together with a letter demonstrating your leadership potential to: Area Management Recruitment, Aldi Stores Limited, Wellington Road, South Marston Park, Swindon, Wiltshire, SN3 4FN.

ALDI AREA MANAGEMENT. IF YOU'RE GOOD ENOUGH, YOU'RE OLD ENOUGH.

"No other retailer gives you so much progression in such a short space of time – within five years I was a Buying Director. I do like the fact I'm responsible for so much and I get real enjoyment from what I do. It's just fantastic."

Julie Ashfield joined the Area Management Programme having graduated in Psychology. The training was very hands-on and Julie did everything from operating cash tills to recruiting store staff. Within 10 weeks, she was providing holiday cover for a Store Manager and had responsibility for a store. After 17 months' training she was then given responsibility for six stores as an Area Manager. In less than five years, she was promoted to Buying Director, responsible for buying 10% of Aldi's UK range.

Of the Aldi Area Management Programme, Julie says "You need to be prepared for hard work both physically and mentally, and need to be flexible. Aldi has delivered on all its promises to me. If I had my time again, I would not change a thing…"

Julie Ashfield, Buying Director

ALLEN & OVERY

Vacancies for around 120 graduates in 2006

For training courses starting in September 2008 and March 2009

 Law

Starting salary for 2006
£29,000

Universities Allen & Overy plans to visit in 2005-6

Birmingham, Bristol, Cambridge, Cardiff, Dublin, Durham, Edinburgh, Essex, Exeter, Leeds, Leicester, London, Manchester, Newcastle, Northumbria, Nottingham, Oxford, Reading, Sheffield, Southampton, Warwick.
Please check with your university careers service for details of events.

Application deadline
See website for full details.

Contact Details

✉ graduate.recruitruitment@
   allenovery.com
☎ 020 7330 3000

Turn to page 192 now to request more information about Allen & Overy.

Allen & Overy is an international legal practice with 4,800 people in 25 major centres worldwide. They are renowned for their high quality Finance and Corporate advice but also have major strengths in areas such as Dispute Resolution, Tax, and Employment.

Within this broad range of expertise they offer a training contract characterised by flexibility and choice. The training programme is widely regarded as the best in the City and continues throughout a career with Allen & Overy.

Allen & Overy offers vacation placements to applicants from both law and non-law backgrounds. These placements offer a valuable insight into a legal career and life at Allen & Overy, giving the chance to take an active role in real deals as well as plenty of opportunities to meet lawyers and trainees.

Allen & Overy recruit 120 trainee solicitors each year and applications are welcomed from both law and non-law candidates. At least a 2:1 degree standard is expected.

Due to the strength of their international Finance and Corporate departments, trainees spend 12 months working in these areas. They also spend time in Dispute Resolution or Employment gaining contentious experience. There are opportunities to undertake international and client secondments. By working closely with their trainers and other colleagues, trainees will develop practical experience and enjoy a high level of early responsibility.

Any reference to Allen & Overy means Allen & Overy LLP and or its affiliated undertakings.

ALLEN & OVERY

▲ Arcadia Group Limited

Vacancies for around 200-250 graduates in 2006

- Finance
- Human Resources
- Logistics
- Purchasing
- Retailing

Starting salary for 2006
£16,800-£23,500

Universities that Arcadia Group plans to visit in 2005-6
London, Loughborough, Nottingham Trent.
Please check with your university careers service for details of events.

Application deadline
Year-round recruitment

Contact Details
Turn to page 192 now to request more information about Arcadia Group.

Recently voted "Most Popular Graduate Recruiter in Retail" (The National Graduate Recruitment Awards 2005) the Arcadia Group is one of the UK's largest fashion retail companies with over 25,000 employees, 2,000 outlets throughout the UK and a growing number of international stores. The group includes eight celebrated high street brands – Burton, Dorothy Perkins, Evans, Miss Selfridge, Outfit, Topshop, Topman and Wallis.

Opportunities for graduates include London head office roles in Distribution, Merchandising, Finance, Buying and HR, and nationwide roles on Arcadia's Graduate Retail Management Programme.

Whichever function graduates join, they are supported to become major contributors to the team. Arcadia are renowned for their commitment to the training and personal development of graduates and learning opportunities include specially designed development programmes, formal courses, support for professional qualifications and on-the-job competency based training.

Rewards include a competitive salary and a great benefits package including up to 25 days holiday, 25% discount on all our exciting brands, sample sales, external discount offers and participation in the company bonus scheme.

Whilst fashion degrees are preferred for our Buying positions, most of our opportunities are open to graduates of any degree. Enthusiasm, initiative and customer focus in addition to a love of fashion are the qualities that make graduates successful at Arcadia. In return graduates are given early responsibility, structured training and development and the opportunity to make an impact on a dynamic business.

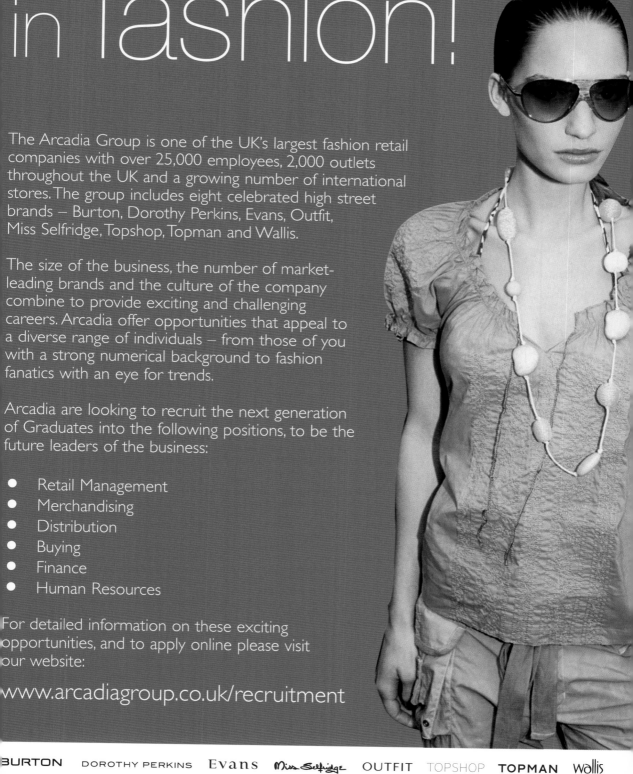

ARMY
BE THE BEST

www.armyofficer.mod.uk

Vacancies for around 900 graduates in 2006

- Accountancy
- Engineering
- Finance
- General Management
- Human Resources
- IT
- Law
- Logistics
- Marketing
- Research & Development

Vacancies also available throughout the world.

Starting salary for 2006
£23,301

Universities the Army plans to visit in 2005-6
Army representatives will be visiting most universities.
Please check with your university careers service for details of events.

Application deadline
Year-round recruitment

Contact Details
☎ 0845 600 1480
Turn to page 192 now to request more information about the Army.

Imagine a career that offers variety, challenge, excitement, management and leadership training, worldwide travel opportunities and a salary rising to £26,280 after one year. If this package appeals, then graduates should consider starting their career as an officer with the British Army, one of the country's largest graduate employers.

The British Army is recognised as one of the best and most professional organisations in the world and engages graduates from all disciplines, developing their management and leadership potential and providing them with the skills and self-confidence to excel when they are in the Army and, later on, in civilian careers.

Key attributes for an officer are personal abilities and aptitude. The Army needs well rounded individuals who are healthy, motivated, self-confident, resilient, who enjoy problem-solving and have strong communication skills. While a degree is a necessary criterion for graduate entry, some officers join straight from school, previous employment or non-commissioned service in the Army.

Initial officer training takes place at the Royal Military Academy Sandhurst and covers all aspects of soldiering, management and leadership training. On completion, graduates will join a Regiment or Corps to undergo specialist training. By this stage, graduates can expect to lead a troop or platoon of an average of 30 soldiers and be responsible for their welfare and operational effectiveness. The Army provides a challenging career, continuous professional development, great promotional prospects, unrivalled travel and sporting opportunities and an excellent remuneration and benefits package.

ARMY OFFICERS ARE TRAINED TO OPEN DOORS MORE EASILY.

As an Army Officer, you're trained to do exceptional things.

To lead and manage under intense pressure. To make tough decisions in unfamiliar territory. To take responsibility for the people under your command, and the millions of pounds worth of equipment they operate.

These are skills that can take you a long way in your Army Career.

They'll also open an awful lot of doors for you afterwards.

ARMY
BE THE BEST

www.armyofficer.mod.uk
Or call 0845 600 1480

ASDA

part of the **WAL★MART** *family*

www.asda.com

**Vacancies for around
70 graduates in 2006**

- Finance
- IT
- Logistics
- Purchasing
- Retailing

Vacancies also available in Europe.

Starting salary for 2006
£21,000

**Universities that ASDA
plans to visit in 2005-6**
Please check with your university
careers service for details of events.

Application deadline
Year-round recruitment

Contact Details
☎ **0113 241 7396**
Turn to page 192 now to request
more information about ASDA.

If graduates are looking for a career where the opportunities are endless and the challenges fresh, ASDA has everything they might want. ASDA is the UK's fastest-growing retailer, with 278 stores, 24 busy distribution centres, 2 ASDA living and 8 George stores. They are also part of the Wal-Mart family, so can offer a fantastic international environment in which to excel.

After joining ASDA, graduates will be an important part of their 140,000-strong UK team, committed to serving more than 13 million customers every week. From day one of ASDA's three-year structured graduate programme (18 months for logistics), graduates will have real responsibility and the chance to contribute their own ideas to the business.

There'll be plenty of support on hand too – starting with an intensive training programme and development opportunities including the possibility of a 12-month international placement to Wal-Mart.

In the long term, graduates will have a personal development programme which will set out their career goals and how to reach them. By year five, ASDA aim to see their graduates take on their first senior management role.

To stay at the top of their game, ASDA are looking for graduates who can demonstrate a real passion for retail and an innovative streak that sets them apart from the competition.

Successful graduates will need commitment, ambition and the drive to help develop the business whilst furthering their career – ASDA are looking to their graduates to be the business leaders of the future.

Manage a team of 50 colleagues in Logistics

Run a £50m store in just five years

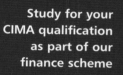

Manage a £50m plus budget as a buyer

Structured three-year leadership graduate programme

Study for your CIMA qualification as part of our finance scheme

January 2004, Fortune Magazine Top European Employer

Our graduate starting salaries are at least £21k

You could be managing a department of 10 colleagues within 6 months

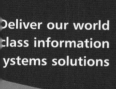
Deliver our world class information systems solutions

Part of the world's largest retailer – WAL-MART

It's only when you hear the facts that you start to see the complete picture. At ASDA, the opportunities are as diverse as our business itself. Whether we're planning a major new store opening or simply reducing the price of one of our best-selling products, we're committed to making sure that everything runs smoothly. And it's graduates like you who are in the driving seat.

Find out more about the huge variety of opportunities available by visiting **www.asda.com**

ASDA
part of the **WAL★MART** *family*

At ASDA we respect all our colleagues and value their differences. We do not tolerate any form of discrimination.

AstraZeneca

Vacancies for around 25-30 graduates in 2006

- Engineering
- Finance
- IT
- Logistics
- Marketing
- Purchasing
- Research & Development

I want to be recognised

Starting salary for 2006
£23,000

Universities AstraZeneca plans to visit in 2005-6
Please check with your university careers service for details of events.

Application deadline
Early December 2005

Contact Details
Turn to page 192 now to request more information about AstraZeneca.

One of the world's leading pharmaceutical companies, AstraZeneca turns great ideas into innovative medicines which make a real difference to people's lives.

The company's excellent reputation and diversity of graduate opportunities makes them the natural choice for candidates from a science background. However, their strengths in manufacturing and commerce mean they can also provide challenges to graduates from other disciplines. Whatever their degree subject, graduates will be excited by the quality and diversity of opportunities. Programmes are designed to progress careers through an integrated range of flexible training activities and blended learning ideas.

From day one induction and personal mentoring to management and global leadership programmes, AstraZeneca provides the resources and support graduates need to reach their full potential; while cross-functional moves, secondments and international assignments can broaden the experience.

It is a performance-based culture with competitive salaries and bonuses that are linked to overall progress. But they also believe that quality of life and quality of work go hand in hand. That's why they actively pursue opportunities for flexible working arrangements.

Core benefits include a minimum level of pension contribution and healthcare provision, and the additional range of 'reward options' is considerable. But these are benefits that people tend to appreciate further down the line.

What probably excites graduates more at this stage is the opportunity to develop their skills within a truly global business that's setting the standards in an industry rich in challenges and rewards.

www.ideas.astrazeneca.com

I want
to go
further

Graduate opportunities, all disciplines.

It's only possible to achieve your full potential when you're given the proper support and resources. At AstraZeneca, we're committed to our graduates' success and reward people on the basis of performance. So if you're looking for a leadership role in science or business, there's no better route to take. **www.ideas.astrazeneca.com**

AstraZeneca
life inspiring ideas

ATKINS

**Vacancies for around
200 graduates in 2006**

■ Engineering

**Starting salary for 2006
£Competitive**

**Universities that Atkins
plans to visit in 2005-6**

Belfast, Birmingham, Bristol,
Cambridge, Cardiff, Dundee,
Glasgow, Heriot-Watt,
Leeds, Liverpool, London,
Loughborough, Manchester,
Newcastle, Nottingham,
Oxford, Plymouth, Sheffield,
Southampton, Surrey,
Swansea.
**Please check with your university
careers service for details of events.**

**Application deadline
Year-round recruitment**

Contact Details

✉ graduates@atkinsglobal.com

☎ 0121 483 6349

Turn to page 192 now to request
more information about Atkins.

As by far the UK's largest engineering consultancy, Atkins is a
leading player in all of the major engineering sectors, including
building design, highways, rail, aviation, water, oil and gas,
power, nuclear, defence and the environment.

The company specialises in planning, designing and enabling major capital
projects, such as modernising and refurbishing 150 stations on the London
Underground, structural design for the M6 Toll road, the development of the
world-famous 7 star Burj al Arab hotel, and many more. Atkins plays a key
role in many of the world's most exciting projects... people are never far from
an Atkins project.

Atkins offers unparalleled opportunities to build a rewarding career across 175
offices in the UK, and overseas, while working with some of the brightest
people in the industry.

The number crunching and calculations students learn at university will be put
into good practice as they learn new techniques to solve problems. Atkins will
back this up with continuing professional development through accredited
training programmes set out by professional institutes, as well as a series of
Graduate Development events for all new starters who join the company.

Talk to anyone at Atkins and students will find that the organisation offers the
broadest range of career paths and the finest personal and professional
development opportunities.

Atkins has graduate positions for civil, structural, aerospace, electrical,
mechanical, computer, building services and geotechnical engineers, in
addition to a variety of science and technical opportunities.

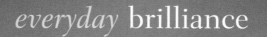

ATKINS

everyday brilliance

graduate opportunities

You are never far from an Atkins project.

As a hotel, the Burj Al Arab (left) is a record breaker. It is both the world's tallest and only 7 star hotel. Widely recognised as a symbol of quality and innovative design, the Burj Al Arab was conceived, planned, designed, engineered and project managed by Atkins.

The project to develop this fabulous hotel is a fine example of the work we undertake around the world. Our clients choose Atkins to **plan, design and enable** their major capital projects.

We can offer you **first rate opportunities** to build your career and work on projects such as this. Our unique **graduate development** programme includes tailored training, and a **£2,500 'golden hello'** with a further £5,000 in options on completion.

To apply for a position, visit our website, or for further enquiries, contact our graduate recruitment resourcer Sarah Warburton, on 0121 483 6349 or at graduates@atkinsglobal.com

www.atkinsglobal.com/graduates

committed to equal opportunities

BAE SYSTEMS

www.graduates-baesystems.com

Vacancies for around 100 graduates in 2006

- Engineering
- Finance
- General Management
- Human Resources
- IT
- Law
- Logistics
- Marketing
- Purchasing
- Research & Development

Starting salary for 2006
£20,800-£25,000

Universities BAE Systems plans to visit in 2005-6

Bath, Glasgow, Heriot-Watt, Lancaster, Leeds, Leicester, Loughborough, Manchester, Nottingham, Nottingham Trent, Sheffield, Strathclyde, Swansea, Warwick.
Please check with your university careers service for details of events.

Application deadline
30th December 2005

Contact Details
☎ 01772 677 277
Turn to page 192 now to request more information about BAE Systems.

In the exciting arena of international aerospace and defence, BAE Systems is a leading player with a wealth of opportunities for undergraduates and graduates. Their business extends globally with a range of programmes in the land, sea and air sectors.

The company recognises that no two people are alike and aim to offer a range of career paths that appeal to a broad range of individuals. They have three graduate entry programmes; 'GDF' is the main graduate programme, 'FLDP' for those looking for a finance leadership career and 'SIGMA' for fast-track international leadership.

'GDF' is the graduate programme that offers training and development alongside on-the-job development. Graduates can use the opportunities of the GDF to develop their own networks across the UK business.

BAE Systems have a large requirement for engineers; in particular, manufacturing & production, mechanical, electrical, systems, project management, microwave and quality. On the business side they are looking for commerical, procurement, project management, marketing and human resources.

Graduates are supported by their line manager and Corporate Mentor. Where appropriate they will also be supported in gaining chartership. The full package offered by BAE Systems includes a competitive salary with six-monthly performance reviews, an initial sign-up payment of £2,000, 25 days' holiday per year and a number of discounted healthcare, car lease and share schemes.

amazing

Engineering, technology, business & finance training

BAE Systems is a truly amazing company.
With 90,000 people in 130 countries, we develop, deliver and support advanced defence and aerospace systems in the air, on land and at sea. Our vision is to be the leading systems company, innovating both to develop new technology and improve the way we work.

If you can turn this vision into reality, we can offer you a stimulating environment, where original ideas see the light of day, and an unrivalled breadth of opportunities in our vibrant, global business.

We offer a choice of schemes. Our two-year Graduate Development Framework (GDF) is our main entry point to careers across a range of engineering,

technology and business functions. But we also offer a Finance Leader Development Programme, a unique five-year scheme to develop our future finance leaders, as well as an intensive, five-year Sigma programme to turn the highest of high flyers into leaders of our international business. Whichever you join, you can expect a valuable mix of on-the-job and external training to build both your technical knowledge and personal skills.

To find out more about our projects and the requirements to join our schemes, and to apply online, go to www.graduates-baesystems.com or call us on 01772 677277 for a copy of our brochure.

BAE Systems helped to produce one of the most advanced multi-role military aircraft ever developed – the Eurofighter Typhoon

BAE SYSTEMS

BAKER & McKENZIE

www.ukgraduates.bakernet.com

Vacancies for around 30 graduates in 2006

For training contracts starting September 2008/March 2009.

Law

Starting salary in 2005
£29,000

Universities that Baker & McKenzie plans to visit in 2005-6

Birmingham, Bristol, Cambridge, Durham, Exeter, Leeds, London, Manchester, Nottingham, Oxford, Warwick.
Please check with your university careers service for details of events.

Application deadline
See website for full details.

Contact Details

 london.graduate.recruit @bakernet.com
☎ 020 7919 1000

Turn to page 192 now to request more information about Baker & McKenzie.

Baker & McKenzie in London offers unparalleled opportunities to become a first class lawyer in the world's largest global law firm. With a network covering 38 countries and a presence in virtually every important financial and commercial centre worldwide, the firm is able to attract the highest quality multi-jurisdictional clients.

Baker & McKenzie look for graduates who are stimulated by intellectual challenge and want to be 'the best' at what they do. Effective communication together with the ability to be creative but practical problem solvers, team players and a sense of humour are qualities which will help candidates stand out from the crowd. In return, the firm provides exceptional training – a commitment which won them 'Best Trainer – Large City Firm' at the LCN-TSG Training and Recruitment Awards 2005.

The two-year training programme commences with an interactive and practical induction focusing on key skills – problem solving, interviewing, presenting and IT. There are four six-month 'seats' which include one in the Corporate department and one contentious. Trainees are given early responsibility on high profile transactions and the opportunity to go on client or international secondments to such places as Sydney, Chicago, Moscow, Hong Kong and Tokyo.

Baker & McKenzie's commitment to training begins even before starting a career with the firm through the London and International Summer Placements. To find out more please visit the website: www.ukgraduates.bakernet.com.

BARCLAYS

www.barclays.co.uk/careers

Vacancies for around 60 graduates in 2006

- Finance
- General Management
- Human Resources
- IT
- Marketing

Starting salary for 2006
£30,000

Universities Barclays Bank plans to visit in 2005-6

Bath, Birmingham, Bristol, Cambridge, Durham, Edinburgh, Leeds, London, Loughborough, Manchester, Nottingham, Oxford, Sheffield, Warwick.
Please check with your university careers service for details of events.

Application deadline
Year-round recruitment

Contact Details

✉ barclays@reed.graduates.
co.uk
Turn to page 192 now to request more information about Barclays Bank.

Throughout their history, Barclays' reputation has been built on a spirit of innovation. They were the first bank to install a computer, the first to issue credit cards and the first to launch ATMs. As such, it's no real surprise that their Business Leadership Programme (BLP) is something special.

Lasting 15 months, the aim of the programme is to give graduates the choice of joining Barclays in their Retail or Corporate Banking businesses, or a function such as Finance, Human Resources, IT and Operations or Barclaycard. It aims to develop graduates into business experts or functional specialists who will become the leaders of tomorrow.

After an initial period in high street banking, graduates then move into their chosen business stream, enjoying real responsibility right from the start. Not that they're pigeonholed though. Barclays believe that the more experience their people gain, the better leaders they'll become.

Training is a key focus of the BLP. As well as developing core skills, there's an array of professional qualifications to work towards. Plus everyone gets £2,000 to spend on training of their own choice. And with Barclays' commitment to career-long learning, this is just the start of their graduates' journey.

Whilst they expect at least 300 UCAS points and a 2.1 honours degree, it's not just academic excellence that they are looking for. Graduates need that special set of qualities that separates them from the usual run-of-the-mill applicants – their energy, ambition, enthusiasm and determination to succeed will set them apart. They want people who are willing to challenge the status quo and embrace everything Barclays has to offer.

BARCLAYS

It is why you never made the same mistake twice.

But there's more to It than just straight forward intelligence. It is about energy. It is about ambition. It is about jumping in with both feet. It is what makes you eager to learn about the world of financial services, and develop your career with a leading FTSE 100 company. It is why you deserve the very best training and development. And It is also why you deserve a higher salary than most. In short, It is the indefinable quality which separates a good graduate from a potential business leader. And It is what we look for here at Barclays. Not everybody has It, but if you think you do, visit www.barclays.co.uk/careers

Have you got It?
The business leadership programme

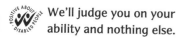 **We'll judge you on your ability and nothing else.**

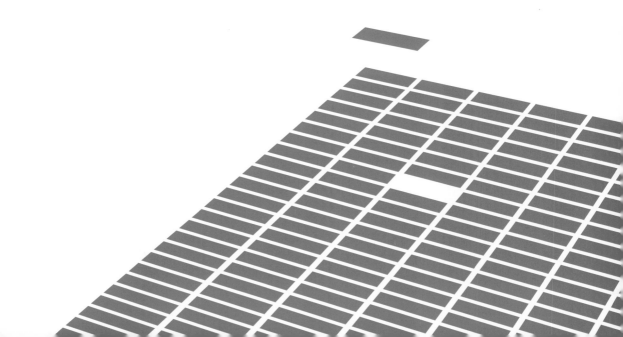

BARCLAYS CAPITAL

www.barclayscapital.com/campusrecruitment

Vacancies for around 300-400 graduates in 2006

- Finance
- Investment Banking
- IT

Starting salary for 2006
£Competitive

Universities that Barclays Capital plans to visit in 2005-6

Cambridge, Edinburgh, London, Oxford, Warwick, York.
Please check with your university careers service for details of events.

Application deadline
30th November 2005

Contact Details
Turn to page 192 now to request more information about Barclays Capital.

Know where you're going. Feel supported. Be noticed.

While many claim to be innovators, this is truly the way Barclays Capital does business and the way the bank applies itself to graduate recruitment. Young and growing, it has enjoyed success and has already cemented a position as a world-leader.

Barclays Capital is the investment banking division of Barclays Bank PLC, one of the largest multi-national financial services groups in the world. Established in 1997, they provide advice, financing and risk management solutions to sovereign, corporate and institutional clients globally.

The graduate programme is key to success and is supported by senior management throughout the organisation. The training starts as soon as an individual accepts a job offer, as they are offered the opportunity to participate in the web-based Global Campus Training Programme, focusing on product education and covering both Credit and Rates modules. It is designed to provide a knowledge of products prior to joining the Graduate Programme.

Once on the programme, graduates are provided with an excellent understanding of financial markets, as well as the bank's products, instruments and services. This creates a strong platform on which to build more specialist expertise. The programme takes learning one step further, incorporating practical applications through a variety of case studies, workshops and presentations.

Depending on the area joined, each person receives comprehensive, role specific training as well as training in soft skills. Barclays Capital enjoys a true meritocracy and flat structure, also encouraging people to obtain appropriate professional qualifications. And that's just the beginning.

Think about
Barclays Capital.

Investment Banking

Think about everything you want from a career, and then ask who can make you the perfect offer. Decide whether you want to work for another firm, or for a firm where we actually do believe that our graduates are the future.

With the support of a parent bank with a balance sheet of over £520 billion, we have offices in 22 countries employing over 7,000 people. Only seven years old, we are expanding every year.

So yes, we are a world leading investment bank, but we are also a meritocracy where the individual is valued, but the team is paramount. We truly believe we are different.

Visit our website for more information.

BARCLAYS CAPITAL

www.barclayscapital.com/campusrecruitment

BBC

www.bbc.co.uk/jobs

Possible Vacancies in 2006

- Accountancy
- Engineering
- Finance
- Law
- Marketing
- Media
- Research & Development

Starting salary for 2006
£Competitive

Universities that the BBC plans to visit in 2005-6
Please check with your university careers service for details of events.

Application deadline
Year-round recruitment

Contact Details

✉ recruitment@bbc.co.uk

☎ 0870 333 1330

Turn to page 192 now to request more information about the BBC.

The BBC aims to be the most creative and trusted broadcaster and programme maker in the world, seeking to satisfy all its audiences worldwide with television, radio and internet services that inform, educate and entertain. In terms of recruitment, it aims to attract an increasingly diverse workforce representative of the population it serves.

The environment new joiners find themselves working in is friendly, welcoming and open to change. Hours are variable and dress code relaxed – it couldn't be further removed from the standard nine-to-five.

Opportunities arise in a wide range of roles. These include journalism, programme making, administration and technical areas. What all areas look for is enthusiasm, motivation and relevant experience, though not necessarily through paid previous employment.

Although intermittently there are advertised training schemes, most graduates tend to enter the BBC through one-off vacancies advertised throughout the year, rarely if ever mentioning possession of a degree as a pre-requisite.

The common denominator for people working at the BBC, regardless of their particular role and where they work in the organisation is a genuine passion for the work they do. The reward for such commitment is the BBC's keen attention to staff development.

People are encouraged to give serious thought to their career planning and training needs, and an attachment system gives staff the opportunity to gain experience in other areas of work.

AS FAR AS YOU'LL GET FROM THE STANDARD 9 TO 5

WHAT DID YOU EXPECT?

Sharing your talent with the BBC is one of the most fulfilling and exciting decisions you can make. After all, you'd be joining an organisation whose consistent innovation and creativity continues to challenge accepted boundaries and win awards around the world. Whatever role you play, you'll apply your imagination and passion to ensuring that we continue to entertain, educate and inform our many diverse audiences.

Everyone wants to find an inspirational place where they'll be encouraged to do things differently. You just have. Visit **bbc.co.uk/jobs** to find out more about the roles available and what it takes to succeed here.

British Nuclear Group

**Vacancies for around
25 graduates in 2006**

- Engineering
- Finance
- Research & Development

Starting salary for 2006
£22,650

**Universities that
British Nuclear Group
plans to visit in 2005-6**
Please check with your university
careers service for details of events.

Application deadline
Year-round recruitment

Contact Details
☎ 01946 786044
Turn to page 192 now to request
more information about
British Nuclear Group.

British Nuclear Group is aiming to become the UK's largest,
most profitable nuclear site management company. The
company is exploring its capabilities in the open market,
balancing profit with principles on projects that matter to
millions of people.

It's a dynamic and evolving organisation with world-class facilities, an expert
talented workforce and cutting edge technology. They are looking for fresh
thinking and innovative graduates from the engineering, science and
commercial community. Opportunities exist in a wide range of roles at
Sellafield site in Cumbria.

Successful graduates join a two-year tailor-made development programme,
ELEMENTS. This offers the chance to develop technical, commercial and
professional skills whilst benefiting from mentor and line management support
and experiencing a real job with real responsibilities. All graduates are
encouraged to achieve chartered or professional status through technical
programmes accredited by many institutions, including the IEE, ICE, IChemE,
IMechE, IOP, RSC and IOM. ELEMENTS will provide an excellent development
toolkit. Career progression depends on individual ability, talent and ambition.

British Nuclear Group's starting salary is competitive. The package of benefits
includes final salary pension scheme, generous holidays, life assurance and a
tax-free welcome award.

British Nuclear Group policy is to treat all company employees and job
applicants fairly, impartially and without prejudice on the basis of race, sex
or disability.

www.bt.com/careers

Vacancies for around 200 graduates in 2006

- Consulting
- Engineering
- Finance
- General Management
- Human Resources
- IT
- Marketing
- Purchasing
- Research & Development
- Sales

Vacancies also available elsewhere in Europe.

Starting salary for 2006
£19,500-£28,000

Universities that BT plans to visit in 2005-6

Aston, Bath, Belfast, Birmingham, Bristol, Cambridge, Durham, Edinburgh, Glasgow, Lancaster, Leeds, London, Loughborough, Manchester, Nottingham, Oxford, Sheffield, Southampton, St Andrews, Warwick.
Please check with your university careers service for details of events.

Application deadline
See website for details.

Contact Details
Turn to page 192 now to request more information about BT.

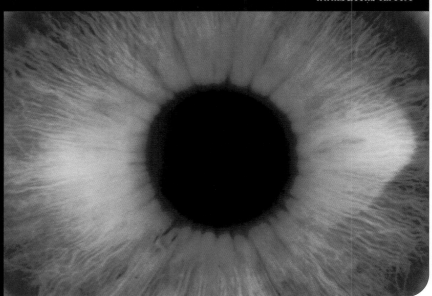

Today technologies are having a profound effect on society and business, transforming the world around us. BT is at the heart of these transformations and is perfectly equipped to meet and satisfy the needs of its customers. IP, broadband, IT, mobile, local, national and international communications, BT designs, develops and delivers them all, helping its customers thrive in a changing world.

BT are looking for ambitious graduates with a fascination for technology and strong leadership skills, who are driven by a desire to impress customers. They offer the challenge of a real role from day one and level of responsibility to build a successful career. The organisation is diverse, so graduates can stay with the company even if they want a change of direction or country.

Graduates need at least a 2.1 degree or international equivalent particularly in Computer Science, General Science, Engineering or Business related subjects, as well as GCSE Mathematics and English Language at grade C or above. Language skills are also welcome as is relevant work experience.

Opportunities range from technical roles in ICT, Engineering and Research and Development, through to business management and commercial roles. Placement opportunities are available for penultimate year students.

The company offers a two-year training and development programme, work shadowing, secondments and special projects can also form part of a flexible package. Graduates are encouraged to gain professional qualifications relevant to their role. BT leads the field in equal opportunities and does not tolerate discrimination of any kind.

Can you imagine unlocking your front door, just by looking at it?

If the answer's yes, you're already thinking about the kinds of things we're thinking about at BT. So, visit us at **www.bt.com/careers** and let's take things further.

BT. Now recruiting for the future.

Cadbury Schweppes

www.cadburyschweppes.com/ukgraduates

Vacancies for around 25 graduates in 2006

- Accountancy
- Engineering
- Finance
- Human Resources
- IT
- Logistics
- Marketing
- Research & Development
- Sales

Starting salary for 2006
£Competitive

Universities that Cadbury Schweppes plans to visit in 2005-6

Aston, Birmingham, Cambridge, Nottingham, Oxford, Oxford Brookes, Warwick.
Please check with your university careers service for details of events.

Application deadline
See website for full details.

Contact Details

✉ csgraduates@csplc.com

Turn to page 192 now to request more information about Cadbury Schweppes.

With more well-loved brands than you can shake a Curly-Wurly at, Cadbury Schweppes have always believed that good values and good business go hand in hand. People all around the globe share a special bond with their products – they love them. And as the ones that make it happen – bringing moments of delight to millions – all 50,000+ Cadbury Schweppes people love it too.

From sampling Dr Pepper to balancing Bertie Bassett's books; testing Trebor mints to engineering Creme Eggs, every new Cadbury Schweppes recruit has the same three things in common – talent, tenacity, and that little bit of craziness. Team these with mammoth investment in training and development, and for graduates with oodles to offer, there's really only one place to go with them. Right to the top. In fact, many of their senior people started as graduates. They've changed Cadbury Schweppes and have been sharing the benefits of a career creating brands that people love ever since.

With real responsibilities and opportunities from day one, graduates get the chance to collaborate and explore with mentors and colleagues – with all they do underpinned by a development programme tailored specially for them. Within the first few years they'll even get the chance to gain experience overseas. Add to that a competitive salary, support in getting relevant professional qualifications, a diverse community of like-minded peers, a great business to work in and amazing brands to champion, and Cadbury Schweppes graduates will be set for one deliciously long-term relationship.

Go to www.cadburyschweppes.com/ukgraduates

creating more than just chocolate.

www.cadburyschweppes.com/ukgraduates

Love,
love,
love.

As one of the world's most
loved brand families, it's in
us in all we do. Our people,
our products, our purpose.

But don't let the sweetness
fool you - as a graduate joining
our Cadbury Schweppes family
you'll have every opportunity
going to make the most of
that big fizzy ambitious streak
and constantly squeeze every
last squeak out of success.
All that, plus a truck-load of
benefits for both your piggy
banks and memory banks. **create. share. love**

Cadbury Schweppes

**Vacancies for around
50 graduates in 2006**

■ Marketing
■ Research & Development

Starting salary for 2006
£Competitive

**Universities that
Cancer Research UK
plans to visit in 2005-6**
Please check with your university
careers service for details of events.

Application deadline
See website for full details.

Contact Details
✉ graduate@cancer.org.uk
☎ 020 7061 8400

Turn to page 192 now to request more
information about Cancer Research UK.

Cancer Research UK is the world's leading independent organisation dedicated to cancer research. Over 3,000 of the world's best doctors, nurses and scientific staff work on their pioneering research. Generating income to support the work that makes them a world-class centre of scientific excellence is no mean feat.

Last year, they raised just over £213 million for their research into cancer – an achievement that underlined the business expertise and commercial vision of their Fundraising and Marketing department. And on joining this team, their graduate trainees are thrust straight to the heart of their activities.

The two-year scheme is designed to offer six-month placements in major fundraising disciplines like Marketing, Communications, Strategy, Event Management, Retail and Community Fundraising. It gives trainees a unique and very broad insight into the organisation and represents the perfect foundation for a career in fundraising.

As a chance to make a difference to the lives of people touched by cancer, a career with Cancer Research UK, obviously, offers plenty in the way of personal fulfilment. But what many people overlook is just how commercially challenging and professionally rewarding their work is.

That's why, although empathy for the cause is essential, it's important to remember that they're looking for business-minded graduates. Ambitious individuals who can help drive fundraising and marketing to new heights.

In addition, they also recruit for their scientific graduate studentships at their London Research Institute. Please see the website for further information.

HEN WE SAY YOU'LL MAKE A
IFFERENCE WE MEAN IT.
IST ASK MOHAMMED.

ammed is the first child in the world to be cured by a pioneering new
ment developed by Cancer Research UK. And it's thanks to groundbreaking
like this that more than 100,000 people with cancer are treated
ssfully every year. To ensure we keep furthering our knowledge, we're
ng for talented graduates to join either of our two graduate programmes.
an choose between our commercially challenging fundraising and
eting graduate scheme, or our scientific research graduate scheme.
way, you'll get the opportunity to make a real difference to people's lives,
developing the skills you need to fulfil your potential.
cancerresearchuk.org/aboutus/

tered charity no. 1089464

CANCER RESEARCH UK

citigroup

www.oncampus.citigroup.com

Vacancies for around 200 graduates in 2006

- Finance
- Human Resources
- Investment Banking
- IT

Vacancies also available throughout the world.

Starting salary for 2006
£Competitive

Universities Citigroup plans to visit in 2005-6
Please check with your university careers service for details of events.

Application deadline
4th November 2005
See website for full details.

Contact Details
Turn to page 192 now to request more information about Citigroup.

Citigroup's goal is to be the most respected global financial services company. No financial institution is more committed to understanding and advancing the financial objectives of its clients.

Citigroup Corporate and Investment Banking has become a market leader, expertly serving the needs of corporations, governments and institutions with a broad range of financial products and services. From stock brokerage to research analysis, investment banking to global transaction services, Citigroup provides more industry-leading solutions to more clients in more countries than any of its competitors.

This is a world-class firm that actively seeks to recruit the best. Working at Citigroup means embracing stimulating and challenging work, being at the centre of the financial industry, and having the chance to have a truly global career. It demands candidates who will thrive in this environment, who have an excellent academic background, the ability to work independently as well as in teams, and perform under pressure. In return Citigroup offer graduates/interns excellent training, a wealth of opportunities and competitive financial rewards.

People who join Citigroup benefit from a rigorous and structured development programme, which is reinforced through on-the-job training and further development opportunities. Training is not something that happens at just at the graduate level, ongoing development is something that is encouraged and supported throughout the firm. Citigroup believes in providing outstanding people with the best opportunity to realise their potential. They recruit into a broad range of business areas and from all degree disciplines.

"I feel privileged to work with the people in my team. It is one of the most exceptional and talented groups of people I have ever and, no doubt, will ever come across. Working with them has allowed me to progress significantly in my understanding of financial analysis as well as my knowledge of specific industry sectors"

ALAN CHOI, ANALYST
INVESTMENT BANKING

apital Markets–
ixed Income & Equities

quity Research

lobal Portfolio Management

lobal Transaction Services

uman Resources

vestment Banking

perations

ales & Trading–
ixed Income & Equities

echnology

Working at Citigroup means being part of a team that is making history in the financial services world. If this appeals to you, come see us. We're looking forward to meeting you.

apply online at **www.oncampus.citigroup.com**

FASTSTREAM ⊙

www.faststream.gov.uk

Vacancies for around 300 graduates in 2006

■ **General Management**

Starting salary for 2006
£23,800

Universities Fast Stream plans to visit in 2005-6
Please check with your university careers service for details of events.

Application deadline
30th November 2005

Contact Details

✉ faststream@parity.net

☎ 01252 776 923

Turn to page 192 now to request more information about Fast Stream.

Imagine affecting the lives of 60 million British citizens; influencing issues that matter. Join the Civil Service Fast Stream and graduates will be doing just that. Making their mark in areas as diverse as health, transport, the environment or education; graduates could be advising a minister, managing and delivering world-class services to the public or purchasing and implementing macro IT solutions.

Fast Streamers are groomed for senior management positions or particular areas such as the European Fast Stream or Clerkships in Parliament. From the outset, graduates will move regularly between projects to acquire a range of business skills . They'll also be given considerable responsibility early on. Later graduates will focus their career on one of three business streams: corporate services, operational delivery or policy delivery – but to reach the top they'll need experience in more than one area.

The Fast Stream is no easy option. Graduates need to be thorough, articulate and persuasive with a minimum 2:2 in any discipline and an intelligent, analytical and open-minded approach. Above all, they'll need to be the kind of person who gets results.

The training programme is exemplary and tailored to meet individual needs. Most departments will pair graduates with a mentor or senior Fast Streamer until they find their feet; graduates can also expect on-the-job training and formal courses. Regardless of gender, ethnic origin, disability, sexuality or marital status, the Fast Stream looks forward to applications from people who have what it takes to make a difference.

IT'S HARD TO GET ON THE PROPERTY LADDER, PARTICULARLY IF YOU'RE A NURSE, TEACHER OR POLICE OFFICER.

BE WHERE IT MATTERS

TO AVOID A KEY WORKER EXODUS, HOUSING MUST BE MADE MORE AFFORDABLE.

agine being at the heart of the most important issues around. Working on a wide variety of topics that can make
e headlines. Shaping the nation's future. This is the life of a Civil Service Fast Streamer.

san Candlish is one of the many Fast Stream graduates whose influence is being felt in the wider world.
e works at the Office of the Deputy Prime Minister, helping to deliver the government's Key Worker Living
ogramme. Her work is enabling society's most valuable people, including nurses, teachers and police officers,
buy or rent affordable housing. Like many Fast Streamers, she's helping to deliver a major initiative.

m playing a key role in ensuring the delivery of the programme under intense political and media scrutiny,
orking closely with both internal and external stakeholders such as the NHS, and helping to manage a
725m budget."

ou want to affect life at every level by joining the Fast Stream (or to read more about Susan's experience),
it www.faststream.gov.uk

ww.faststream.gov.uk

CIVIL SERVICE
FASTSTREAM

CLIFFORD CHANCE

Vacancies for around
120 graduates in 2006
For training contracts starting in
August 2008 and February 2009.

 Law

Starting salary for 2006
£29,000

Universities that
Clifford Chance
plans to visit in 2005-6
Belfast, Birmingham, Bristol,
Cambridge, Durham,
Edinburgh, Exeter, Leeds,
London, Manchester,
Nottingham, Oxford,
Sheffield, Southampton,
St Andrews, Warwick, York.
Please check with your university
careers service for details of events.

Application deadline
Year-round recruitment

Contact Details
✉ graduate.recruitment@
    cliffordchance.com
☎ 020 7006 6006

Turn to page 192 now to request more
information about Clifford Chance.

Clifford Chance is a truly global law firm, which operates as one organisation throughout the world. Their aim is to provide the highest quality professional advice by combining technical expertise with an appreciation of the commercial environment in which their clients work.

As a trainee lawyer graduates will gain breadth and depth in their experiences. Clifford Chance offers a uniquely global perspective and actively encourage their lawyers to develop international experience. Most trainees interested in an international secondment spend six months abroad.

With offices in 19 countries, the firm operates across all business cultures and offers full service advice to clients in key financial and regulatory centres in Europe, the Americas and Asia. Clifford Chance's lawyers advise internationally and domestically, under both common and civil law systems. Their working style is characterised by a real sense of energy, enthusiasm, and determination to provide the best possible service to their clients.

They commit to building the futures of all their trainees, and their recruitment strategy is based on a long-term view. They want graduates to stay with them on qualification, and enjoy a rewarding career contributing to the success of the global business.

They are a diverse multicultural firm and expect and encourage their trainees to develop in directions that reflect their individual talents and style. Throughout their training contract, the firm will give trainees the opportunity to realise their highest ambitions and become part of their commitment to be the world's premier law firm.

Closing M&A deal

Providing pro bono advice

Opening negotiations

Involved in a dispute resolution

Milestone memories

The Clifford Chance training contract will qualify and prepare you to do rather more than provide quality legal advice. We equip our people with the skills to deliver insightful and far-reaching client solutions and to do so in a pragmatic and professional way. So we won't just help you gain technical skills and a professional qualification. The contract will offer experience milestones that will provide firm foundations for your entire career. In return, we will expect you to commit fully to an aim we all share – to be the world's premier law firm.

www.cliffordchance.com/gradsuk

Our world at your feet

C L I F F O R D
C H A N C E   We have a global commitment to diversity, dignity and inclusiveness.

corus

www.corusgroupcareers.com

Vacancies for around 125 graduates in 2006

- Engineering
- Finance
- Human Resources
- Logistics
- Purchasing
- Research & Development

Vacancies also available in Europe.

Starting salary for 2006
£18,000-£20,500

Universities that Corus plans to visit in 2005-6

Bath, Birmingham, Bristol, Cambridge, Cardiff, Durham, Lancaster, Leeds, Liverpool, Loughborough, Manchester, Newcastle, Nottingham, Oxford, Sheffield, Strathclyde, Swansea. **Please check with your university careers service for details of events.**

Application deadline
Year-round recruitment

Contact Details

 recruitment@corusgroup.com

☎ 01926 488025

Turn to page 192 now to request more information about Corus.

Corus will provide the opportunity to learn, develop, gain experience, broaden horizons and make an impact. They have the scope to provide individually tailored careers that will be interesting, challenging and dynamic with commitment to professional accreditation, joint career ownership and real work projects from the outset. The starting package includes; quarterly bonus, interest-free loan and 35 days holiday.

In order to achieve the aim of being a world-class company, people who can set goals and surpass them are essential; people with drive, enthusiasm, ideas, commitment, flexibility, imagination and resilience. Successful graduates are those who benchmark their own achievements against those of peers, respect the community around them and simply work hard.

Corus is renowned for creating value. Company culture is one of continuous improvement and open communication with a strong focus on safety and sustainability. Corus has changed considerably over the past few years and this change is set to continue; a 2004 turnover of £9.3 billion, profit of £582 million and entry into the FTSE100.

Corus is developing modular housing to help meet the need for affordable homes. A joint venture innovation, "Assure", is enabling the creation of the world's first antibacterial fridge. Corus "Minelifta" aids the safe clearing of land-mine sites. The Eden Project, Millennium Stadium, Airbus A380, Trafford Centre, new Mini, Twickenham, Heathrow Terminal 5 and new Wembley Stadium, all have Corus expertise and metal in common.

More information including graduate profiles, is available online.

CREDIT SUISSE | FIRST BOSTON

www.csfb.com/standout

**Vacancies for around
190-200 graduates in 2006**

- Finance
- Investment Banking
- IT

Starting salary for 2006
£Competitive

**Universities that CSFB
plans to visit in 2005-6**
Bath, Bristol, Cambridge,
City, Dublin, Durham
London, Oxford,
Warwick, York.
Please check with your university
careers service for details of events.

Application deadline
18th November 2005

Contact Details
✉ graduate.recruitment@
csfb.com
Turn to page 192 now to request
more information about CSFB.

Credit Suisse First Boston (CSFB) is a leading global investment bank serving institutional, corporate, government and individual clients. Its businesses include securities underwriting, sales and trading, investment banking, private equity, financial advisory services, investment research, venture capital, correspondent brokerage services and asset management.

CSFB operates in 69 locations in 33 countries across five continents. CSFB is a business unit of the Zurich-based Credit Suisse Group, a leading global financial services company. Its commitment to providing outstanding service to clients, their focus on teamwork, diversity and excellence means recruitment of the best and brightest people is essential to the firm's success.

Five areas of the business at CSFB recruit graduates: Corporate & Investment Banking; Fixed Income; Equities; Finance, Administration & Operations; and Information Technology. Each area offers different roles depending on candidates' qualifications, personality and interests. An in-depth explanation of each of these divisions can be found on the CSFB website.

CSFB considers its training to be truly exceptional in every area. Graduates who join as analysts can expect a two-three month induction programme, followed by ongoing structured development in their first few years. The more focused and motivated the graduate is, and the more they take ownership for their own training, the faster they will develop at CSFB.

Interns will also benefit from exposure to senior management and training in financial markets, as well as having the chance to socialise with colleagues and fellow interns.

IT IN.

t's not about having a degree n finance.

TAND OUT.

t's about having a degree of curiosity.

CREDIT SUISSE | FIRST BOSTON

onvertibles, derivatives, equities, securities, hedge funds. Don't worry if they're all Greek to u. Many people join us without being fluent in investment banking. If you're curious and arn fast, you'll soon pick up the vocabulary you need to thrive in your chosen business area. tting in at CSFB isn't about how much you know right now: it's about how much you can d in the future.

ww.csfb.com/standout

CSFB | EMPOWERING CHANGE:

CONNECTION

www.dataconnection.com/careers

Vacancies for around 20 graduates in 2006

■ IT

Starting salary for 2006
£26,000
Plus initial one-off payment of £4,000.

Universities that Data Connection plans to visit in 2005-6
Cambridge, Edinburgh, Oxford, St Andrews, Warwick.
Please check with your university careers service for details of events.

Application deadline
Year-round recruitment

Contact Details
✉ recruit@dataconnection.com
☎ 020 8366 1177
Turn to page 192 now to request more information about Data Connection.

Data Connection is an internationally renowned computer technology company, specialising in the exciting world of telephony and data communications. Its leading-edge software and hardware products are used by some of the biggest names in the telecommunications and IT industry, such as BT, Microsoft and Cisco. In 2005, they have been voted fifth in The Sunday Times 100 Best Companies to Work For.

Opportunities are available in a wide range of challenging roles. Graduates' initial focus will be technical, after which they could find themselves in charge of the design for an innovative new product, managing a world-class project team, offering expert advice to customers, or taking on sales and marketing.

The company looks for exceptional people with an outstanding academic record, including all A grades at 'A' level and a good degree. Prior computing experience is not necessary, but an enquiring mind and the ability to understand and solve complex problems is.

Data Connection cares passionately about employee development and believes in taking talented individuals, nurturing them and working with them to fulfil their potential. Its culture is all about 'doing difficult things well' – and that includes the way they manage and develop their people.

Training is ongoing, and specifically tailored to meet each individual's needs and objectives. Graduates have a constant high level of support and assistance from their assigned mentor and manager who allocate around fifty days of their time to the graduate's training in the first year alone. This is a massive, and probably unique, level of training investment.

Doing Difficult Things Well –

and being Well Rewarded

Data Connection's culture is all about doing difficult things well. This applies to the communications and telephony technology we design, market and sell, how we manage and develop our people and the way we focus on getting the work/life balance right.

We also reward ourselves well. Data Connection is owned by an Employee Benefit Trust which pays out our profit, currently £8.5million, to our 300 employees based on their performance and contribution. This is in addition to our competitive salary and benefits package.

To find out more:

- visit www.dataconnection.com
- email us at recruit@dataconnection.com
- call us on 020 8366 1177

Data Connection, 100 Church Street, Enfield EN2 6BQ.

Deloitte.

**Vacancies for around
1200 graduates in 2006**

- Accountancy
- Consulting
- Finance
- IT

Starting salary for 2006
£Competitive

**Universities that Deloitte
plans to visit in 2005-6**

Aberdeen, Aston, Bath,
Belfast, Birmingham, Bristol,
Cambridge, Cardiff, City,
Dublin, Durham, East
Anglia, Edinburgh, Exeter,
Glasgow, Heriot-Watt,
Lancaster, Leeds,
Leicester, Liverpool,
London, Loughborough,
Manchester, Newcastle,
Nottingham, Oxford,
Reading, Sheffield,
Southampton, St. Andrews,
Strathclyde, Warwick, York
Please check with your university
careers service for details of events.

Application deadline
Year-round recruitment

Contact Details

✉ gradrec.uk@deloitte.co.uk

☎ 0800 323 333

Turn to page 192 now to request
more information about Deloitte.

Deloitte offers graduates stimulation and reward in professional
services. They're the only 'big 4' firm maintaining consultancy
as a core service and are winning more complicated full service
assignments as a result.

Deloitte delivers expertise in Audit, Tax, Consulting and Corporate Finance in a
uniquely collaborative manner that draws on talent from across the firm. In
doing so they create individual client teams that can attend to any challenges
our clients face. So, no matter what discipline graduates practice, they'll rub
shoulders with countless other Deloitte individuals, all experts in their own field.

Exercising individual talent is the life-blood of the firm. Deloitte takes people
who are great, and makes them exceptional. Their first class training and
development programmes are effectively bespoke, guaranteeing graduates
will become highly competent and well-rounded business professionals
with rich career prospects.

Deloitte has 10,000 bright individuals working for them in the UK. All that talent
makes Deloitte a particularly invigorating place to work. Its working ethos
balances hard work with 'having a life' outside of work. They believe in plain
speaking, pragmatic thinking and delivering on their promises, to each other
and to their clients. All of which makes Deloitte one special place to work.

Deloitte recruits graduates with a minimum of 300 UCAS tariff points and a
predicted or obtained 2:1 in any discipline. Deloitte welcomes applications for
deferred entry and recruits nationwide.

Apply online at www.deloitte.co.uk/graduates. For Consulting, the deadline is
31 January 2006.

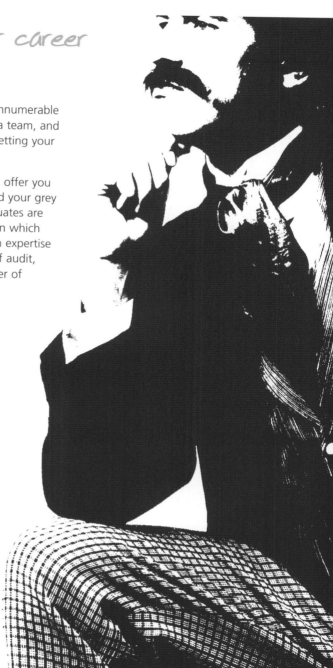

Feed your mind.

How would you like your career – well done?

Fed a diet of first-class training, top-drawer clients and innumerable opportunities to excel, both as an individual and within a team, and it's easy to see a career at Deloitte is something worth getting your teeth into.

As the fastest growing professional services firm, we can offer you unparalleled career opportunities to stimulate and reward your grey matter. Our training and development schemes for graduates are first class and, thanks to the uniquely collaborative way in which we work, you'll participate in team projects that draw on expertise and experience from across the firm's key service areas of audit, tax, consulting and corporate finance. There are a number of undergraduate opportunities on offer as well, from our Summer vacation schemes to our Insight days which showcase what working at Deloitte is really like.

If you've been predicted or obtained a 2:1 and have at least 300 UCAS tariff points under your belt, visit **www.deloitte.co.uk/graduates** where you'll find plenty more information to chew on.

We recruit from any discipline, welcome applications for deferred entry and recruit nationwide.

Deloitte.

Audit . Tax . Consulting . Corporate Finance .

Deutsche Bank

www.db.com/careers

Vacancies for around 600 graduates in 2006

- Accountancy
- Finance
- Human Resources
- Investment Banking
- IT

Starting salary for 2006
£Competitive

Universities Deutsche Bank plans to visit in 2005-6
Please check with your university careers service for details of events.

Application deadline
1st December 2005
See website for full details.

Contact Details
☎ 020 7545 3033
Turn to page 192 now to request more information about Deutsche Bank.

Deutsche Bank has been a global player for more than 135 years, from financing the building of the Baghdad Railway in the 19th century to being the first German bank to list on the NYSE in 2001.

Today, it is a financial services provider, top executor of M & A deals, Europe's number 1 fund manager and the global leader in securities trading. Deutsche Bank's success has also been recognized by industry surveys; it has been named Credit Derivatives House of the Year 2004, World's Best Risk Management House and World's Best Foreign Exchange House by leading publications in the past year. It also offers holistic advisory services to private clients and much, much more.

At Deutsche Bank 'A Passion to Perform' is more than just a claim – it's the way it does business, attracting the brightest talent to deliver an unmatched franchise. It is committed to being the best financial services provider in the world. Its breadth of experience, leading-edge capabilities and financial strength create value for all its stakeholders: clients, investors, employees, and society as a whole.

Even though the Bank continues to evolve, the key to Deutsche Bank's success remains constant: a focus on client needs, a spirit of innovation, a broad range of expertise combined with technological power and financial strength delivered by diverse, highly skilled professionals across the globe.

Deutsche Bank is continually visiting the leading campuses around the world searching for talent. It is looking for fresh ideas, innovative solutions and an entrepreneurial spirit.

Your vision: To keep achieving your goals.
Our promise: The opportunity to succeed.

Graduation is the fulfilment of a long-held aspiration - but it is just the beginning. At Deutsche Bank you'll be given opportunities to achieve your goals, time and again. As one of the world's leading financial institutions, we provide the platform to take your career further. Join us in: Controlling - Global Banking - Global Markets - Human Resources - Operations - Private Wealth Management - Risk Management - Technology.

Expect the better career.

Find out more at **www.db.com/careers**

A Passion to Perform. **Deutsche Bank**

DIAGEO

www.diageospirit.com

**Vacancies for around
20 graduates in 2006**

- Engineering
- Finance
- Logistics
- Marketing
- Purchasing
- Sales

Starting salary for 2006
£Competitive

**Universities that Diageo
plans to visit in 2005-6**

Aberdeen, Aston, Bath,
Belfast, Birmingham,
Cambridge, Dundee,
Durham, Edinburgh,
Glasgow, Heriot-Watt,
Manchester, Nottingham,
Oxford, St Andrews,
Strathclyde, Warwick.
Please check with your university
careers service for details of events.

Application deadline
30th November 2005

Contact Details

✉ graduates@diageospirit.com
Turn to page 192 now to request
more information about Diageo.

Diageo is the world's leading premium drinks company with an unrivalled collection of beverage alcohol brands across spirits, wine and beer categories. They are a young, vibrant organisation with prestigious brands such as Smirnoff, Guinness, Archers, Baileys and Gordon's – recognised and enjoyed the world over.

And whilst Diageo is proud of their brands, they're also extremely proud of their people. People at Diageo are different. Why? Well it's something about the spirit within – an almost indefinable quality that is inherent in everyone at Diageo. In its simplest terms, it could be described as a passion for what they do, but equally it's so much more than that...

It's about being innovative and constantly searching for new ideas that drive growth. They never stand still – always learning, questioning and improving – constantly setting high standards... and then trying hard to exceed them.

Diageo people have a burning energy that spurs the growth of both the business and themselves. It's a driving emotion, so real that it's almost tangible and if graduates join them they'll recognise it immediately – as it's something that's already inside them.

They blend the balance of working hard with a strong team atmosphere that makes work a pleasure. And whilst graduates will have fun they'll be expected to deliver results, as first and foremost, Diageo is a world-class business.

This is the spirit of Diageo... and they want graduates to be part of that. Information on Diageo and the graduate recruitment programme can be found on www.diageospirit.com.

DIAGEO

THE SPIRIT OF DIAGEO

If we could, we'd bottle it

The feeling you get at Diageo is like nothing else. It's that intangible something that makes us so unique. It gives us the energy to live life to the full and the drive to succeed. But it's impossible to describe in a few short words. If you've already got it in you, you'll know exactly what we mean.

If you've got the right spirit, we can offer you extraordinary career opportunities and superb training & development across Marketing, Sales, Finance, Supply Chain, Engineering, Technical, Procurement, Production & Packaging and a range of commercial roles. For more information, and to apply, visit our website.

DRINKAWARE.CO.UK

www.diageospirit.com

DLA PIPER RUDNICK GRAY CARY

Vacancies for around 85 graduates in 2006

For training courses starting in 2008

 Law

Starting salary in 2005
£16,000-£29,000
Varies by region.

Universities DLA Piper plans to visit in 2005-6

Aberdeen, Birmingham, Bristol, Cambridge, Cardiff, Dundee, Edinburgh, Exeter, Glasgow, Leeds, Leicester, Liverpool, London, Manchester, Newcastle, Nottingham, Oxford, Sheffield, Strathclyde, Warwick.
Please check with your university careers service for details of events.

Application deadline
31st July 2006

Contact Details
✉ recruitment.graduate@ dlapiper.com
☎ 020 7796 6677

Turn to page 192 now to request more information about DLA Piper.

DLA Piper is one of the world's largest full service legal services providers. Over 2,800 lawyers across 50 offices in 18 countries provide a broad range of legal services through their global practice groups. The firm is built to meet the ongoing needs of clients, wherever they choose to do business. These clients include some of the world's leading businesses, governments, banks and financial institutions.

The firm has appeared in The Sunday Times survey of the '100 Best Companies to Work For' for the last five years, and also holds the 'Investors in People' accreditation, demonstrating commitment to its employees and their ongoing development. As well as its own people, DLA Piper has an extensive Corporate Social Responsibility programme to support local communities around each office, this includes pro-bono work as well as educational and environmental projects.

DLA Piper welcomes applications from students with either a law or non-law background who have a minimum of 3 Bs at A-Level and a 2.1 degree classification (expected or achieved). The firm looks for highly motivated and energetic team players with sound commercial awareness, outstanding communication and organisational skills, and, above all, an appetite for life!

Trainees complete four six-month seats and progress is monitored through regular reviews and feedback. The in-house Professional Skills Course, tailored to the needs of DLA Piper's trainees, combined with high quality on-the-job experience means each trainee gains an excellent grounding on which to build their professional career.

Be different...

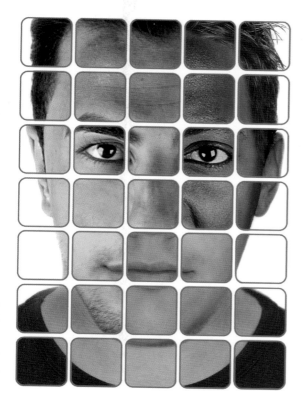

Be yourself...

Be part of...

DLA Piper Rudnick Gray Cary – one of the largest global legal services organisation in the world – and we're still growing! Our impressive client base, combined with the emphasis on high quality service and teamwork, provide a challenging fast paced working environment.

We have offices in Birmingham, Edinburgh, Glasgow, Leeds, Liverpool, London, Manchester and Sheffield as well as 42 international locations in a further 17 countries across Asia, Europe and the US. Our current vision is to be a top five global, full service law firm.

To find out more about our summer vacation placement scheme or our training contracts, please visit our website **www.dlapiper.com**

DLA Piper Rudnick Gray Cary adheres to the Law Society's Voluntary Code to Good Practice in the Recruitment of Trainee Solicitors

[dstl]

www.dstl.gov.uk/careers

Vacancies for around 100 graduates in 2006

▮ Engineering

▮ Research & Development

Starting salary for 2006
£Competitive

Universities that Dstl plans to visit in 2005-6
Bath, Birmingham, Bristol, Cambridge, Durham, Edinburgh, Exeter, Leeds, London, Loughborough, Manchester, Nottingham, Oxford, Sheffield, Southampton, St Andrews, Strathclyde, Warwick, York
Please check with your university careers service for details of events.

Application deadline
Year-round recruitment

Contact Details
✉ graduates@dstl.gov.uk
☎ 01980 614596
Turn to page 192 now to request more information about Dstl.

JUST THINK...

Dstl, the Defence Science and Technology Laboratory, is an integral part of the Ministry of Defence (MOD) as its trusted adviser on defence related science and technology.

Its work spans the spectrum of science, yet much of it remains confidential. This is because, by delivering innovative research, providing specialist technical services and tracking global technological developments, its role is to protect our national security and the safety of our Armed Forces.

As part of an evolving, high-tech organisation that is respected worldwide, graduates are encouraged to think beyond conventional scientific boundaries. They work on projects that matter to millions, in world-class facilities and alongside 3,000 of the finest minds in their fields.

Enthusiastic and analytically minded graduates are recruited throughout the year from the following disciplines: applied sciences, physical sciences, engineering, biological & health sciences, systems analysis, operational research. All will be flexible self-starters with an enquiring mind, good interpersonal skills and the ability to work independently or within a team.

Dstl offers a chartership scheme to help graduates gain membership of a relevant professional body, sponsorship to take further qualifications, and a 'buddy' scheme to offer advice and guidance. Through its partnerships with industry and NATO allies, UK and overseas secondments are also a realistic prospect. But while graduates' careers will be a priority, flexible hours will ensure they enjoy a healthy work/life balance. Starting salaries are designed to attract high achievers, while comprehensive benefits include a choice of final salary or stakeholder pension schemes and good sports and leisure facilities.

THINK. THINK BURNING ISSUES. THINK EXTREMES. THINK PYROTECHNICS. THINK WHITE HOT. [THINK -25°.] THINK GLOBAL WARMING. THINK RISING TIDES. THINK LIQUID CRYSTAL DISPLAYS. THINK HEALTH SCREENING. THINK TESTING TIMES. THINK TIME OF YOUR LIFE.

Ideas that stretch the boundaries of scientific and technological thinking. Classified work that goes to the edge of the defence spectrum and beyond. Pioneering solutions that address the burning issues of today [often with international partners such as our Swedish counterparts]. Civil Service careers for science and technology graduates and postgraduates that offer stimulating projects, overseas secondments, great benefits and a healthy work/life balance. Just join Dstl. www.dstl.gov.uk/careers

Dstl is part of the Ministry of Defence

[dstl]   JUST THINK...

ERNST & YOUNG

www.ey.com/uk/graduate

**Vacancies for around
550 graduates in 2006**

- Accountancy
- Consulting
- Finance
- IT

Starting salary for 2006
£Competitive

**Universities Ernst & Young
plans to visit in 2005-6**

Bath, Birmingham, Bristol,
Cambridge, City, Durham,
Edinburgh, Exeter, Glasgow,
Lancaster, Leeds, Liverpool,
London, Loughborough,
Manchester, Newcastle,
Nottingham, Oxford,
Sheffield, Southampton,
St Andrews, Surrey,
Warwick, York.
Please check with your university
careers service for details of events.

Application deadline
Year-round recruitment

Contact Details

  gradrec@uk.ey.com

☎ 0800 289 208

Turn to page 192 now to request more
information about Ernst & Young.

Ambition
It's a state of mind

Ernst & Young helps businesses and organisations to improve their effectiveness and achieve their objectives. They do this by providing their clients with a range of expert services – from Auditing & Tax to Advisory Services, from Corporate Finance to entrepreneurial business development, from economic analysis to information systems advice and assurance.

The firm's clients include many of the world's most successful companies, together with government, entrepreneurs, small businesses, charities and other organisations throughout the UK.

Ernst & Young is looking for those who have the drive to succeed. Our programmes are based on real experience, with graduates working on live client projects from day one. Graduates are given a wide range of support and career development opportunities, including formal training, career counselling, coaching, mentoring and knowledge-management resources. The firm's Accelerated Development Programme enables their highest performers to rapidly develop and advance their careers.

Ernst & Young receive many applications, but offer only 550 graduate positions and 300 undergraduate positions each year. Their selection process is rigorous with priority given to candidates who have the right balance of skills and personality, with a clear interest in their business and the drive and ambition to succeed.

To find out more about who Ernst & Young are, what they do and what they're looking for, visit www.ey.com/uk/graduate. Gather the knowledge needed there, then go to the online application form for completion and submission.

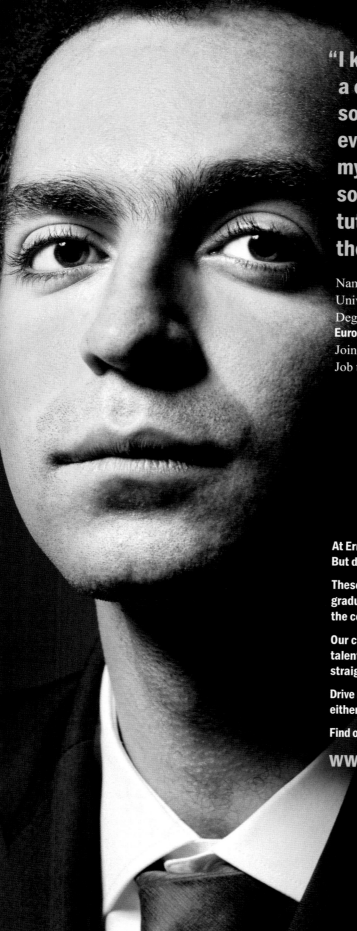

"I knew I wanted variety and a challenge, to keep learning something new and useful every day, to be taken out of my comfort zone and take on something that my family, my tutors and my friends never thought I'd be able to pull off."

Name: **Subhi Sherwell**
University: **Oxford**
Degree: **Modern History and Russian (MA), European Literature (M.St)**
Joining date: **September 2002**
Job title: **Executive, Corporate Finance (TAS)**

At Ernst & Young we believe you can teach many things. But drive and ambition are not amongst them.

These are the key qualities that we look for in all our graduates, and they help to differentiate us from the competition.

Our clients always expect us to develop the best available talent, and we offer genuine challenges and opportunities straight away to recruits with the right approach.

Drive and ambition are values that can't be taught – you either have them or you don't.

Find out more about us, and the opportunities open to you, at:

www.ey.com/uk/graduate

EVERSHEDS

Picture shows our annual (Easter) Big Deal event involving first year university students in an international joint venture event. See website for details.

Recognised as one of the world's leading law firms, Eversheds is a success story, with an innovative approach to the way it does business. Trainees are the future of the firm. Each person counts, as an individual, because clients do business with people they respect and like. Being a successful commercial lawyer is all about developing an enthusiastic and pragmatic approach to finding the best commercial solution for one's client.

Eversheds looks for individuals who have three qualities: intellectual ability – a flexible and enquiring mind; the potential, with training, to develop a real commercial awareness; and most important of all, a positive attitude. Clients are looking for winners, people they can trust and rely on to give them real solutions to complex business needs.

Right from the outset, the firm invests in its graduates. A blend of on-the-job training, specialist courses and secondments to clients and other offices is designed to suit each individual, thus developing knowledge, practical skills and confidence. Real leadership giving direction, support and encouragement is always on hand.

Trainees are expected to use their initiative and, under proper supervision, are given as much responsibility as they can take. There is a great emphasis on client contact throughout their training and career.

Eversheds has a genuinely friendly culture. The environment is professional, supportive and fun!

Graduate opportunities at Eversheds

Welcome to life in the fast lane

At Eversheds we don't believe in hanging about when it comes to graduate training. The best way for you to learn is to throw you into the thick of the action (with all the support you need to deal with it). As an international law firm, we'll provide you with interesting work from day one. We'll constantly challenge you with more responsibility and we'll expect you to challenge us back.

We are looking for high achievers who want a fast-track to a great career in a friendly, dynamic environment. If that sounds like you, please visit our website www.eversheds.com **for further information and to apply on-line.**

www.eversheds.com

ExxonMobil

Vacancies for around 30 graduates in 2006

- Engineering
- Finance
- Human Resources
- IT
- Marketing
- Sales

Starting salary for 2006
£27,000

Universities ExxonMobil plans to visit in 2005-6

Bath, Birmingham, Bristol, Cambridge, Edinburgh, Exeter, Heriot-Watt, Leeds, London, Loughborough, Manchester, Nottingham, Nottingham Trent, Strathclyde, Surrey.
Please check with your university careers service for details of events.

Application deadline
Year-round recruitment

Contact Details

☎ 0845 330 8878
Turn to page 192 now to request more information about ExxonMobil.

ExxonMobil is a worldwide leader in the petroleum and petrochemicals business and has a presence in nearly 200 countries and territories.

Exxon Mobil Corporation is the parent company of the Esso, Mobil and ExxonMobil companies that operate in the United Kingdom. The business is dynamic, strategically important and exciting. To secure their position within this environment the company strives towards operational excellence with an expert talented workforce, strong financial resources and cutting edge technology. Their customers are both global and local, ranging from major airlines to the individuals who visit their service stations worldwide.

A diverse range of career opportunities are available within both commercial and technical functions where graduates can expect immediate responsibility and accountability. Analytical skills are essential, as is the ability to think, act and adapt in a global environment with sound judgment and tenacity.

The two-year ExxonMobil Graduate Development Programme is run in conjunction with the London Business School covering interpersonal skills, business awareness and people management leading to alumni status of the LBS.

Input from supervisors helps graduates develop an appropriate career path by reviewing their skills and training needs. All graduates develop technical and personal skills via internal, external courses and on-the-job training. Graduates are also encouraged to achieve chartered qualifications where appropriate.

Rapid skills growth and career development is standard and graduates can expect a high degree of intellectual challenge and change.

In the next 25 years the demand for energy will increase by as much as 50%.

www.exxonmobil.com/ukrecruitment

It's a challenge like no other.
And it will be solved by someone like you.

The need for energy is a very real economic issue. It affects literally everyone – everywhere in the world. At ExxonMobil, we're uniquely positioned to help find the answers to the world's toughest energy challenges. We have the resources, the technology, and the commitment of people just like you.

When you build your career here, you have the opportunity to make a profound impact. From inventing new technologies, to unlocking new sources of petroleum, to developing more efficient fuel and engine systems, you can make the breakthroughs happen.

The biggest challenges attract the best. Whether your background is in business, engineering, or science, ExxonMobil has a challenging career waiting for you.

Esso   Mobil

ExxonMobil
Taking on the world's toughest energy challenges.

FRESHFIELDS BRUCKHAUS DERINGER

Vacancies for around 100 graduates in 2006

For training contracts starting in August 2008 and February 2009.

■ Law

Starting salary for 2006
£29,500

Universities Freshfields Bruckhaus Deringer plans to visit in 2005-6
Birmingham, Bristol,
Cambridge, Cardiff,
Durham, Exeter,
Leeds, Leicester,
London, Manchester,
Newcastle, Nottingham,
Oxford, Sheffield,
St Andrews, Warwick.
Please check with your university careers service for details of events.

Application deadline
31st July 2006

Contact Details
✉ graduates@freshfields.com
☎ 020 7427 3194
Turn to page 192 now to request more information about Freshfields Bruckhaus Deringer.

Freshfields Bruckhaus Deringer is a leading international law firm. Through its network of 27 offices in 17 countries, the firm provides first-rate legal services to corporations, financial institutions and governments around the world.

The firm's lawyers work on high profile, interesting and often ground-breaking work for clients such as Hewlett Packard, DaimlerChrysler, Deutsche Bank, P&O and the Bank of England.

The firm recruits about 100 people each year to start as trainee solicitors in its London office. Whatever commercial area attracts a graduate's interest, there is a good chance the firm has a thriving practice in that area, and it is recognised as a market leader for a wide range of work.

There is no such thing as a 'typical' Freshfields lawyer. The firm's broad array of practice areas and clients demands a wide range of individuals with differing skills, abilities and interests. However, graduates will need strong academic qualifications, a broad range of skills and a good record of achievement in other areas.

The firm's trainees receive a thorough professional training in a very broad range of practice areas, an excellent personal development programme and the chance to work in one of its international offices or on secondment with a client in the UK or abroad.

The firm has 120 places on its Easter and summer vacation schemes for penultimate year undergraduates. Applications are taken between 1 December and 31 January. For further information see their website at www.freshfields.com/graduates.

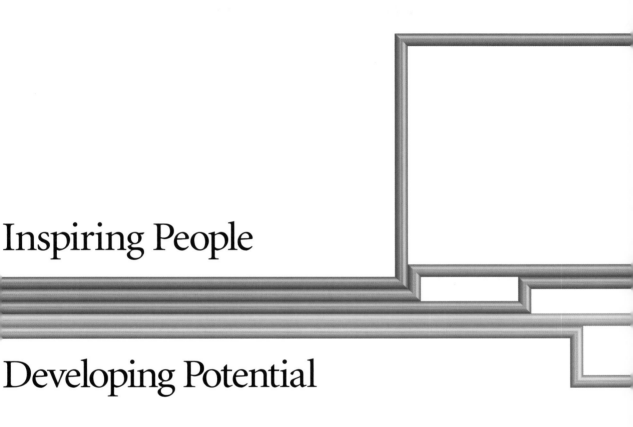

FRESHFIELDS BRUCKHAUS DERINGER

Inspiring People

Developing Potential

Trainee Solicitors London

Training at Freshfields Bruckhaus Deringer isn't just about becoming a lawyer. It's about exploring and maximising your individual potential.

As a trainee, we'll expect a great deal from you. But we also understand that you'll be expecting a lot from us.

We'll give you high-quality training alongside your international colleagues and you'll be working with and learning from some of the most talented lawyers in the world. Your training contract will be unique to you. You'll get the blend of support and freedom you need to evolve your career and take advantage of the opportunities our international network offers.

The work here is world-class. We handle a wide variety of interesting, innovative matters for high-profile clients. We have a friendly and relaxed atmosphere and are committed to helping you keep your life in balance.

To find out more, visit the graduate recruitment pages on our website and request a copy of our graduate recruitment brochure.

www.freshfields.com/graduates

Vacancies for around
200 graduates in 2006

☐ **General Management**

☐ **IT**

Starting salary for 2006
£19,008-£27,253

Universities that GCHQ
plans to visit in 2005-6
Please check with your university
careers service for details of events.

Application deadline
Year-round recruitment

Contact Details

✉ recruitment@gchq.gsi.gov.uk

Turn to page 192 now to request
more information about GCHQ.

Everyone's heard about MI5 and MI6. Well, GCHQ is the third axis of Britain's intelligence service. Using some of Europe's most powerful and advanced computing infrastructure, their role is to gather vital electronic and digital intelligence – often in code – and then to decode it, analyse it, piece it together, and pass it on in useable form to the Government, military and law enforcement agencies.

This intelligence is then used to inform military operations, to foil international arms and drugs crime, or to counter acts of terror. Within GCHQ, CESG (the UK National Technical Authority for Information Assurance) provides expertise and consultancy which makes sure the UK's own IT infrastructure remains secure from hackers and other external threats. Though a low profile organisation by choice and necessity, GCHQ plays a vital and influential front-line role in protecting the interests of Britain and British people.

GCHQ employs over 4,500 people – mainly at their brand-new HQ in Cheltenham, but also at other sites across the UK and overseas. This diverse team includes IT and electronics specialists, mathematicians, linguists, information scientists and intelligence analysts – as well as all the support roles graduates would expect: in business support, finance and accountancy, project management and purchasing.

GCHQ recruits throughout the year. All employees enjoy a heavy investment in personalised training, support towards professional qualifications, mentoring, shadowing and the chance to switch career paths and disciplines right through their career.

CAFE LAVILLE 01:09:23   9/1/05 14:03

CHELTENHAM. GLOUCESTERSHIRE

IT WAS THE

WoMan

sIPPING hEr

CoffEE

The woman reading the newspaper has been involved in an illegal arms deal. What do you think her exact role was? You can make a guess, but as one of the UK's three intelligence services it's GCHQ's business to know. So we'll tell you. As a graduate Linguist she helped monitor conversations between two international suspects. We recruit and train people of graduate calibre into a number of areas, including languages, mathematics, finance, information technology, electronics and communications as well as for fast-track, intelligence and general management roles. So don't assume the work won't be for you. For information on the range of opportunities visit **www.gchq.gov.uk/recruitment** Our recruitment campaigns start in October and continue throughout the year. Closing dates vary, so please check our website regularly (you can apply online). Applicants must be British citizens.

Careers in British Intelligence

GlaxoSmithKline

www.gsk.com/careers

Vacancies for around 40 graduates in 2006

- Engineering
- Finance
- IT
- Marketing
- Purchasing
- Research & Development
- Sales

Starting salary for 2006
£Competitive

Universities that GSK plans to visit in 2005-6
Please check with your university careers service for details of events.

Application deadline
See website for full details.

Contact Details
✉ ukuniversity_relations@gsk.com
☎ 020 8047 4777

Turn to page 192 now to request more information about GSK.

GlaxoSmithKline (GSK) is a place where ideas come to life. As one of the world's leading research-based pharmaceutical companies, GSK is dedicated to delivering products and medicines that help millions of people around the world do more, feel better and live longer.

Based in the UK, but with operations in the US and 117 other countries worldwide, GSK enjoys a 7% share of the world's pharmaceutical market, with sales of £20.3 billion in 2004. And much of this is thanks to an extensive product range that includes everything from prescription medicines to popular consumer healthcare products.

So while some people depend on GSK's pioneering pharmaceutical products to tackle life-threatening illnesses, others choose best-selling nutritional brands such as Lucozade and Ribena to help them enjoy an active life. GSK even manages to brighten smiles with some of the world's favourite toothpastes.

New starters at GSK will soon see that there's no such thing as a typical career path. With roles for undergraduates, graduates and postgraduates, as well as a number of industrial placements, across all business functions, there are plenty of opportunities to grow and develop.

And with so much geographical and business diversity on offer, GSK is in a great position to give all the support needed. There are no limits on where a career could lead – in fact, the UK Graduate Development Programmes and graduate direct entry have produced some of GSK's most senior managers. Find out more about the opportunities on offer by visiting GSK at www.gsk.com/careers.

www.gsk.com/careers

Improving lives is in our nature, we'll do the same for you

Graduate Opportunities

Sales and Marketing, Finance, R&D, Science, IT, Procurement, Regulatory Affairs, Global Manufacturing and Supply

People all over the world look to GlaxoSmithKline for a healthier future, and we take pride in helping them live longer, feel better and do more. But it's not just the people that use our products who get to enjoy everything we have to offer. Our wide-ranging graduate opportunities will give your career the best possible start, whatever your skills may be. And as well as plenty of exposure to major business challenges, you'll also enjoy a competitive salary and personalised benefits package.

For a full listing of current opportunities, please visit our website at www.gsk.com.
All data processed in accordance with the provisions of the Data Protection Act.
GSK is proud to promote an open culture, encouraging people to be themselves and giving their ideas a chance to flourish.
GSK is an equal opportunity employer.

Together we can make life better.

www.gs.com/careers

Vacancies for around
250 graduates in 2006

  Finance

  Human Resources

  Investment Banking

  IT

Vacancies also available throughout the world.

Starting salary for 2006
£Competitive

Universities that
Goldman Sachs
plans to visit in 2005-6
Bath, Birmingham, Bristol, Cambridge, City, Dublin, Glasgow, Leeds, London, Loughborough, Manchester, Nottingham, Oxford, Reading, St Andrews, Warwick.
Please check with your university careers service for details of events.

Application deadline
9th November 2005
See website for full details.

Contact Details
Turn to page 192 now to request more information about Goldman Sachs.

Goldman Sachs is a leading global investment banking, securities and investment management firm, providing a full range of investing, advisory and financing services worldwide to a substantial and diversified client base, which includes corporations, financial institutions, governments and high-net-worth individuals. In doing so, it brings together people, capital and ideas to make things happen for its clients.

Goldman Sachs recruits the best students from a wide range of university courses and backgrounds. Academic discipline and understanding of finance are less important than the personal qualities an individual brings with them. It is intellect, personality and zest for life that the firm values the most. It recognises that having a diverse workforce encourages increased creativity and innovation. This is crucial to improved performance and continued business success. To that end, it is committed to increasing an environment that values diversity and promotes inclusion.

Goldman Sachs' ability to meet challenges and ensure the firm's success in the future depends on attracting and retaining the highest quality people and the firm takes an unusual effort to identify the best person for every job. It evaluates candidates on six core measures – achievement, leadership, commercial focus, analytical thinking, teamwork and the ability to make an impact. It expects commitment, enthusiasm and drive but in return offers unparalleled exposure, early responsibility, rewards and unlimited career opportunities. Goldman Sachs recruits finalists into its analyst programme and penultimate year students into its summer internship programme.

Graduate to even greater challenges.

If you thrive on challenging yourself to the fullest extent, you will find a team of similarly driven colleagues here to help take your abilities and talents to the next level.

www.hbos-choices.co.uk

Vacancies for around 95 graduates in 2006

Accountancy

Finance

General Mangement

Human Resources

IT

Retailing

Starting salary for 2006
£Competitive

Universities that HBOS plans to visit in 2005-6
Please check with your university careers service for details of events.

Application deadline
See website for full details.

Contact Details
✉ hbos@workcomms.com

Turn to page 192 now to request more information about HBOS.

HBOS plc was established in 2001 as a result of the merger between the Bank of Scotland and Halifax plc. Instantly, HBOS became one of the largest financial services organisations in Europe with an unrivalled 22 million customers and a relationship with two out of every five households in the UK. Last year we recorded profit before tax of over $4.7 billion and are currently the UK's leading mortgage and savings provider.

The HBOS name may not be instantly recognisable to consumers but their brands most certainly are! The market-leading line-up of brands includes award-winning companies like Esure, Clerical Medical and Intelligent Finance.

As one of the UK's leading financial organisations, HBOS are keen to continue their success internationally. There is currently a buzz of activity in their Australian and European operations as they aim for significant growth in these markets in 2006.

HBOS have a huge presence in the UK community not only through the products and services they provide, but by employing more than 70,000 people. HBOS are therefore committed to strengthening and adding value to these communities where they live and work – from working alongside local community groups, to supporting national groups and projects.

For graduates, the exact nature of opportunities depends on which of the diverse business areas they join, and which specialist career path they choose – each scheme is tailored to the needs of the business area and their own professional aspirations.

Seriously good choice

Graduate opportunities across the UK in:

Business Management
Corporate Banking
Asset Management
Financial Markets
Finance
Technology
Risk

Choosing a graduate programme is a pretty daunting task. The company may be a familiar high-street name, but will they actually offer you the opportunities you're looking for?

In choosing a scheme and an employer, you want to know the decision you make will lead onto further choices, to a wide range of opportunities opening out in front of you. Joining HBOS means just that – beginning a journey where you will keep on making choices, in an organisation whose breadth and strength offer the opportunity to develop your skills and experience in so many different ways.

In fact, the challenge with such an array of options is knowing where to start. So check our website **www.hbos-choices.co.uk** to help you find the best fit. It gives you an outline of the business areas within the HBOS group, and a taste of what life is like for people who have already made the choice that you are considering.

Now it's up to you. So go on – choose.

www.hbos-choices.co.uk

The world's local bank

Vacancies for around 400 graduates in 2006

- Finance
- General Management
- Investment Banking
- IT
- Logisitics
- Retailing
- Sales

Vacancies also available throughout the world.

Starting salary for 2006
£17,000-£35,000

Universities that HSBC plans to visit in 2005-6

Aston, Bangor, Bath, Birmingham, Bristol, Brunel, Cambridge, Cardiff, City, Durham, Edinburgh, Essex, Exeter, Glasgow, Hull, Keele, Kent, Lancaster, Leeds, Leicester, Liverpool, London, Loughborough, Manchester, Newcastle, Northumbria, Nottingham, Oxford, Oxford Brookes, Sheffield, Southampton, Stirling, Surrey, Warwick, York.
Please check with your university careers service for details of events.

Application deadline
Year-round recruitment
See website for full details.

Contact Details

✉ uk.recruitment@hsbc.com

Turn to page 192 now to request more information about HSBC.

HSBC is one of the largest banking and financial services organisations in the world. It has a network of over 9,800 offices in 77 countries and territories in Europe, the Asia-Pacific region, the Americas, the Middle East and Africa.

HSBC provides a comprehensive range of financial services to more than 110 million customers: personal financial services; consumer finance; commercial banking; corporate, investment banking and markets; and private banking.

Exceptional graduates of any discipline are recruited onto HSBC's world class training programmes that prepare them for management and executive positions across the business.

These include Actuarial, Branch Banking, Business Management, Executive Management, Insurance Broking, Information Technology, International Management, Investment Banking and Wealth Management and Private Banking. HSBC also offers internships to promising undergraduates in their penultimate year of study. Internships are available in a wide range of branch and business area locations

HSBC is committed to certain key business principles and values. In addition to providing appropriate financial products and following fair, responsible lending policies, HSBC has a strong corporate social responsibility programme that contributes to the everyday life of local communities. Employees are encouraged to get involved in HSBC's many educational and environmental projects across the globe.

To find out more about the opportunities that HSBC can offer and to apply online, visit www.hsbc.com/graduates.

There are many ways to spot talent

And one site where talent is spotted

hsbc.com/graduates

If you're ambitious, academically successful and determined to make the most of life, every graduate recruiter will be interested in what you have to offer. So why should you choose to join HSBC?

HSBC is successful in developing talented people. We know you expect the finest training, and to be rewarded for your personal contributions to HSBC's success. We know you want the challenges of early responsibility and decision-making.

As a world leader in banking and financial services, we need the best of the new generation of graduates to take us into the future. Proven ability is rewarded with increased responsibility. From your first day, we train you to be an expert in your chosen field.

We look far and wide for our ideal colleagues, as you do for the ideal job. Make your choice a little easier, have a look at www.hsbc.com/graduates

HSBC

The world's local bank

www.ibm.com/employment/uk/graduates

**Vacancies for around
100 graduates in 2006**

- Consulting
- Finance
- IT
- Sales

Starting salary for 2006
£25,000-£28,000

**Universities that IBM
plans to visit in 2005-6**
Please check with your university
careers service for details of events.

Application deadline
Year-round recruitment

Contact Details
✉ graduate@uk.ibm.com
Turn to page 192 now to request
more information about IBM.

IBM is the world's leading information technology and consulting services company, with over 90 years of leadership in helping businesses innovate. They help clients in many industries leverage the new era in business – on demand. Their extensive list of clients include British Airways, eBay, HMV and The Wimbledon Championships.

In 2005 IBM won The Times IT Graduate Employer of choice and the Target National Graduate Recruitment Awards most popular recruiter in the IT and communications industry.

IBM recruits graduates into a wide range of areas including Consulting, Software Development, IT, Finance and Sales. As the opportunities are vast, so IBM has developed a career planner to give graduates all the information they need to map their career from day one. IBM has a comprehensive induction programme designed to equip graduates with the tools to do their job. After completion of this, personal, business or technical skills training is provided as and when required.

The company is committed to creating an inclusive working environment, that embraces diversity. IBM is committed to creating a flexible work environment that sets it apart from their competitors. Employees are given the tools and rewarded on the value they provided – not the time spent in the office.

To be considered graduates should have a minimum of 300 UCAS points and have achieved or be expecting a 2:1 or higher. IBM looks for great team players and excellent communicators with first class analytical skills and high personal drive.

EASONS to choose IBM #275

No one title could cover my job.

Business Technology Consultant, Data Modeller, Event Co-ordinator. However we refer to you at IBM, you won't be seen as just a graduate trainee. To find out more about real business exposure that starts the day you do, visit: **ibm.com**/employment/uk

TARGET
National Graduate Recruitment Awards 2005

Winner

**Vacancies for around
50 graduates in 2006**

- Engineering
- Finance
- General Management
- Human Resources
- IT
- Marketing
- Purchasing
- Research & Development
- Sales

Vacancies also available throughout
Europe and Asia.

Starting salary for 2006
£23,000-£26,000

**Universities that ICI
plans to visit in 2005-6**
Aston, Bath, Birmingham,
Bristol, Cambridge, Cardiff,
Durham, Edinburgh,
Glasgow, Heriot-Watt,
Leeds, London,
Loughborough, Manchester,
Newcastle, Nottingham,
Oxford, Sheffield,
Strathclyde, Warwick.
Please check with your university
careers service for details of events.

Application deadline
Year-round recruitment

Contact Details
✉ grad_recruitment@ici.com
Turn to page 192 now to
request more information about ICI.

With over 33,000 employees in over 50 countries worldwide the
ICI Group is a global leader in formulation science, applying
groundbreaking science and technology to develop,
manufacture and sell the products and ingredients that define
what is seen, touched, smelt and tasted every single day.

ICI has, and continues to build, a portfolio of businesses that are leaders
within their respective industries, bringing together outstanding knowledge
of customer needs with leading edge technology platforms and products
that provide superior performance.

ICI is looking for the vital ingredient, the most talented graduates in Europe
who can drive a significant part of what the business does today and in
the future. In return, ICI can equip its talent with the training, motivation,
environment and opportunity to excel – and create a uniquely rewarding
career.

ICI is looking for truly outstanding individuals – graduates with the potential to
become the next generation of business leaders and help shape the future of
the businesses in Europe and China.

ICI offers a range of opportunities giving graduates the choice of joining one
of its diverse global businesses in a comprehensive selection of functions.
With either a passion for research, a head for business, a skill for
management, a love of technology, a flair for engineering or a talent for
working with people, ICI has positions in every area of expertise or interest.

Go to http://www.icigraduates.com to see where ICI's opportunities meet
graduates' aspirations.

JPMorgan

Vacancies for around
350 graduates in 2006

■ Finance
■ Investment Banking
■ IT

Starting salary for 2006
£Competitive

Universities JPMorgan
plans to visit in 2005-6
Bristol, Cambridge,
Dublin, London,
Manchester, Oxford.
Please check with your university
careers service for details of events.

Application deadline
27th November 2005
See website for full details.

Contact Details
Turn to page 192 now to request
more information about JPMorgan.

JPMorgan believe that they are the most challenging and rewarding career choice a talented graduate can make. They call this the 360° career because it is a total package of earning power, job satisfaction and personal development.

JPMorgan is the investment banking business of JPMorgan Chase, a leading global financial services firm, which has assets of $1.2 trillion and a hundred and sixty thousand people in more than fifty countries. In February 2005 JPMorgan's UK investment banking business completed a joint venture with Cazenove's investment banking business to become JPMorgan Cazenove, one of the UK's foremost investment banks. JPMorgan serves the interests of clients with complex financial needs, from major corporations and governments to charities and private individuals.

JPMorgan take graduates of all disciplines into a range of different businesses from Investment Banking to Technology. Our training programmes combine on-the-job learning with top-quality classroom instruction and practical experience gained in different parts of the business. As well as a thorough grounding in a chosen business area, JPMorgan gives graduates broad experience to the wider commercial picture and a range of transferable business skills, from project management to team leadership.

JPMorgan are looking for team-players and future leaders with exceptional drive, creativity and personal qualities. Academic credentials are important, but so are your achievements outside the classroom.

You will find more information about graduate careers and internship opportunities at 360career.com

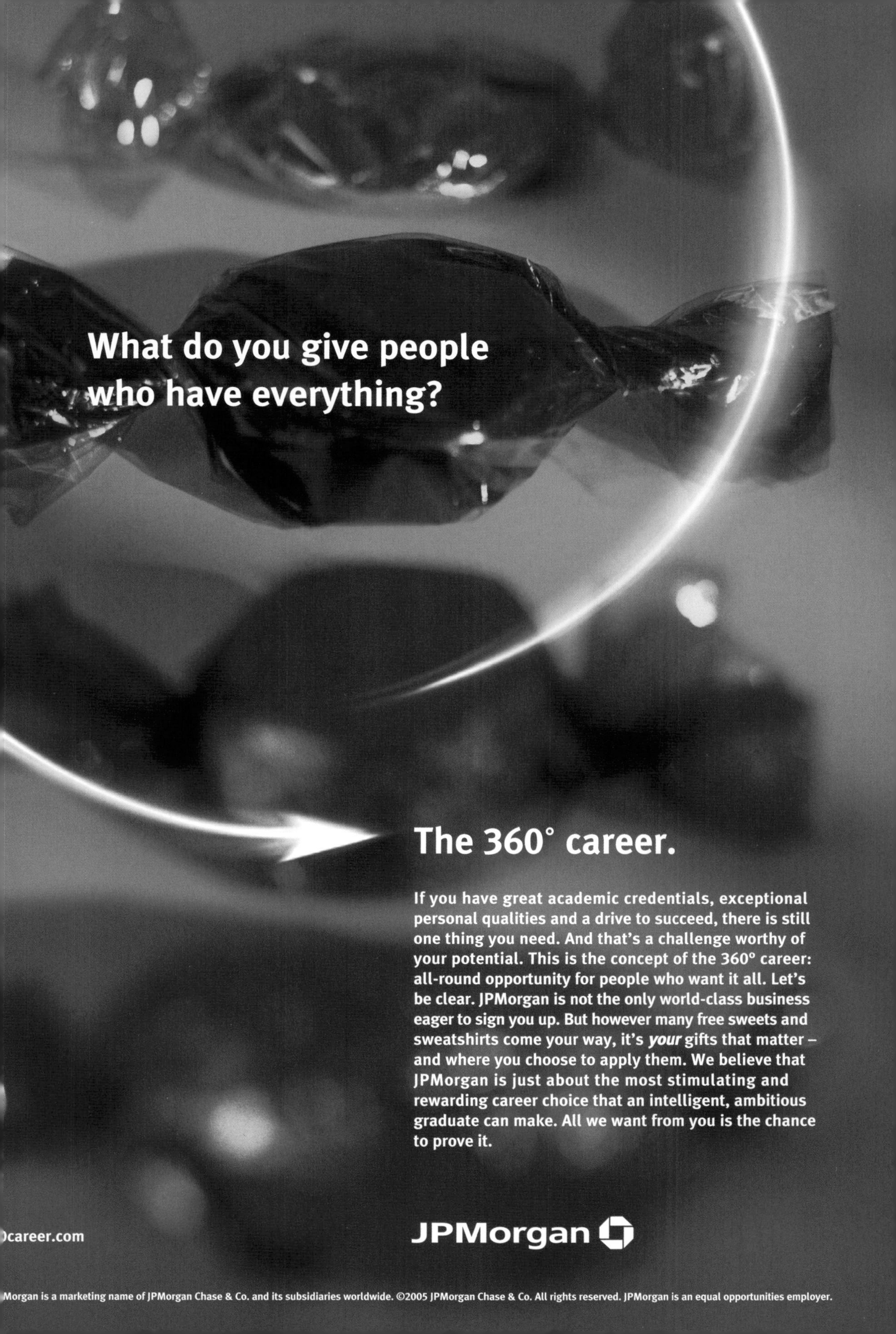

What do you give people
who have everything?
The 360° career.
If you have great academic credentials, exceptional personal qualities and a drive to succeed, there is still one thing you need. And that's a challenge worthy of your potential. This is the concept of the 360° career: all-round opportunity for people who want it all. Let's be clear. JPMorgan is not the only world-class business eager to sign you up. But however many free sweets and sweatshirts come your way, it's *your* gifts that matter – and where you choose to apply them. We believe that JPMorgan is just about the most stimulating and rewarding career choice that an intelligent, ambitious graduate can make. All we want from you is the chance to prove it.
career.com
JPMorgan
Morgan is a marketing name of JPMorgan Chase & Co. and its subsidiaries worldwide. ©2005 JPMorgan Chase & Co. All rights reserved. JPMorgan is an equal opportunities employer.

**Vacancies for around
800 graduates in 2006**

- Accountancy
- Finance
- Human Resources
- Marketing
- Sales

Are you destined for greater things?

Starting salary for 2006
£Competitive

**Universities that KPMG
plans to visit in 2005-6**
Bath, Birmingham, Bristol,
Cambridge, Cardiff,
Durham, Edinburgh, Exeter,
Glasgow, Leeds, London,
Manchester, Newcastle,
Nottingham, Oxford,
Sheffield, Warwick, York.
Please check with your university
careers service for details of events.

Application deadline
Year-round recruitment

Contact Details
✉ ukfmgraduate@kpmg.co.uk
☎ 0500 664665
Turn to page 192 now to request
more information about KPMG.

KPMG in the UK is part of an international network of business advisers, with almost 100,000 people working in nearly 150 countries. They operate at the heart of business, using teamwork and diversity of thought to find suitable solutions for our broad range of clients. KPMG's advice can help keep FTSE companies running profitably and can influence the outcome of crucial board meetings.

KPMG can help graduates develop the skills they need to work with clients and to pass the exams crucial to their longer-term career. But the brightest graduates pick KPMG for more reasons than the excellent all-round training. They like the culture, the honest approach, the sense of community and the people. People who share a passion for delivering the very best service for their clients.

KPMG are looking for exceptional graduates to join them within their Audit, Tax and Advisory practices. There are 23 offices around the UK and there are over 20 different graduate career paths to choose from. This year KPMG has also added opportunities in their support functions such as Human Resources, Marketing and Sales.

To apply graduates must have at least 300 UCAS Tariff points (260 UCAS Tariff points for the ACCA Audit programme), be on course for at least a 2:1 degree and have gained a grade A at GCSE Maths (grade B for Tax and ACCA Audit programme). Graduates don't need a business or economics degree, KPMG recruit from any discipline.

For more information and to apply on-line, visit www.kpmg.co.uk/brightminds.

**It was
destined for
greater things**

**If you are too,
apply to KPMG**

If you're really bright, we expect you'll be looking for a career that really stretches you, that gives you the opportunity to achieve greater things. Join KPMG in the UK and you'll be challenged from the start.

We are one of the leading firms of business advisers and right now we're looking for the brightest graduates to join us. We have 23 offices across the UK and over 20 different graduate career routes to choose from. You'll have responsibility early on and the chance to work at the heart of business, on real projects with real clients, from governments to retail outlets to charities.

So if you are hungry for a career that will push you to your full potential, apply online at www.kpmg.co.uk/brightminds

We are an equal opportunity employer and value diversity in our people.

**AccountancyAge
Awards 2004
WINNER**

**THE SUNDAY TIMES
10
BEST BIG
COMPANIES
TO WORK FOR
2005**

AUDIT ■ TAX ■ ADVISORY

KPMG

WORLD LEADER IN BEAUTY PRODUCTS

Vacancies for around 25-30 graduates in 2006

- Engineering
- Finance
- Logistics
- Marketing
- Sales

Starting salary for 2006
£Competitive

Universities that L'Oréal plans to visit in 2005-6
Aston, Bath, Bristol, Cambridge, Cardiff, Durham, Edinburgh, London, Manchester, Nottingham, Oxford, Swansea, Warwick.
Please check with your university careers service for details of events.

Application deadline
16th December 2005

Contact Details

✉ HR@uk.loreal.com
Turn to page 192 now to request more information about L'Oréal.

One of the world's most dynamic FMCG companies, L'Oréal is worldwide number one in cosmetics, launching over 500 new products throughout the world every year. L'Oréal is an Investor in People, employing 52,000 people in 130 countries.

L'Oréal are looking to recruit true entrepreneurs with creative flair and drive who can bring their real life experiences to a dynamic and passionate working environment.

Each year L'Oréal recruits 25 to 30 of the most talented graduates onto their Graduate Development Programme, into five disciplines: Commercial, Marketing, Logistics, Finance and Engineering. The year-long individually tailored development programme provides on-the-job placements in different related business areas supported by structured learning. Graduates are expected to make a tangible contribution while increasing their skills and knowledge. How far and how fast they progress is based on talent and performance.

60-80 Internships are also available every year at L'Oréal for students and graduates. Alongside these two programmes L'Oréal runs two international competitions for students: The L'Oréal Marketing Award "Brandstorm" offers undergraduates the chance of being International Brand Managers and designing a new product/range; The e-Strat Challenge gives an insight into General Management, using an online simulation to increase a company's share price index by taking strategic decisions.

Taking part in either of their business games, or undertaking an internship with the company, can often be the first step to a career with L'Oréal.

TO BUILD BEAUTY, WE NEED TALENT.

"BEAUTY IS ENTREPRENEURSHIP. WORKING IN A TEAM OF PASSIONATE AND DYNAMIC INDIVIDUALS BRINGS OUT THE BEST IN ME."

Richard H.

NATIONAL ACCOUNT CONTROLLER, L'ORÉAL UK

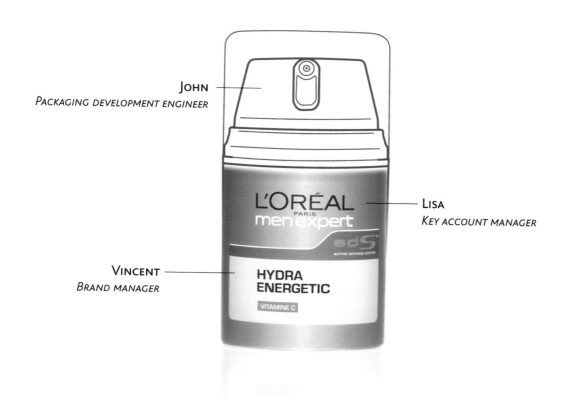

JOHN
PACKAGING DEVELOPMENT ENGINEER

LISA
KEY ACCOUNT MANAGER

VINCENT
BRAND MANAGER

L'ORÉAL
WORLD LEADER IN BEAUTY PRODUCTS

JOIN US. WITH 52,000 EMPLOYEES IN MORE THAN 130 DIFFERENT COUNTRIES, EVERY YEAR L'ORÉAL LAUNCHES 500 NEW PRODUCTS THROUGHOUT THE WORLD.

GRADUATE DEVELOPMENT PROGRAMME. LIKE YOU, WE ARE RESULTS FOCUSED AND HAVE OPPORTUNITIES AVAILABLE IN COMMERCIAL, MARKETING, FINANCE, LOGISTICS AND ENGINEERING. WE ARE OFFERING GRADUATES A TAILOR-MADE DEVELOPMENT PROGRAMME WHICH INVOLVES THREE ON-THE-JOB PLACEMENTS SUPPORTED BY STRUCTURED LEARNING. RESPONSIBILITY FROM DAY ONE, THE SUPPORT OF A MENTOR, PERSONALISED FAST-TRACK CAREERS WITH INTERNATIONAL OPPORTUNITIES, COMPETITIVE COMPENSATION AND BENEFITS. WE ARE LOOKING FOR TRUE ENTREPRENEURS WITH CREATIVE FLAIR AND DRIVE WHO CAN BRING THEIR REAL LIFE EXPERIENCES TO A DYNAMIC AND PASSIONATE WORKING ENVIRONMENT.

MORE INFORMATION ON THIS PROGRAMME, INTERNSHIPS AND OUR BUSINESS GAMES: **WWW.LOREAL.CO.UK**

Linklaters

www.linklaters.com/careers/ukgrads

Vacancies for around
130 graduates in 2006
For training contracts starting
September 2007/March 2008.

■ Law

Starting salary for 2006
£29,700

Universities Linklaters
plans to visit in 2005-6
Please check with your university
careers service for details of events.

Application deadline
See website for full details.

Contact Details
✉ graduate.recruitment@
        linklaters.com

Turn to page 192 now to request
more information about Linklaters.

Linklaters is a law firm that advises the world's leading companies, financial institutions and governments on their most challenging transactions and assignments. Their work is divided into three main areas – Corporate, Finance & Projects and Commercial.

They recruit graduates in both law and non-law disciplines. Those graduates who don't have a law degree take the Graduate Diploma in Law (GDL) conversion course, which involves a year at law college. The next step is the year-long Legal Practice Course (LPC) which all trainees have to complete before they begin their training contracts.

The training contract itself is built around four six-month seats or placements. The seat system gives trainees front-line exposure to a range of practice areas. This develops versatile, well-rounded lawyers, but it also gives trainees a good idea of the kind of law they want to do when they qualify. There are also opportunities for client secondments or overseas placements throughout the training contract.

This is a firm that achieves exceptional things for clients, but it is also a supportive community in which individuals are encouraged to be themselves. Ask anyone from Linklaters what they most enjoy about the firm, and the answer is usually the same: "It's the people".

Training with Linklaters means working alongside some of the world's best lawyers on some of the world's most challenging deals. They expect a lot of their graduate trainees, but the rewards – personal and professional as well as financial – are very high indeed.

Things I wish I'd known.

Linklaters could be the ideal place to launch your career as a business lawyer, but you won't know until you've had the chance to find out about us. One thing you can be sure of, though: it's usually the people with the best information who make the best career choices.

This is why we have packed our website with the insights and observations of graduates who have already joined Linklaters. Not so long ago they were sitting where you are now: with the luxury of hindsight, they can answer your questions, even those you haven't thought of yet.

Find out what it's really like to train as a lawyer at Linklaters. Enjoy a candidate's-eye-view of our selection process. Experience the ups and downs of a big deal. Develop a sense of what your future colleagues might be like. Everything you need to know is at

www.linklaters.com/careers/ukgrads

Linklaters

Lloyds TSB

www.adarkhorse.com

Vacancies for around 100 graduates in 2006

- Accountancy
- Finance
- General Management
- Human Resources
- Investment Banking
- IT
- Marketing
- Retailing

Starting salary for 2006
£24,000-£28,450

Universities Lloyds TSB plans to visit in 2005-6
Birmingham, Cardiff, Durham, Edinburgh, Leeds, Loughborough, Manchester, Nottingham, Sheffield, Warwick.
Please check with your university careers service for details of events.

Application deadline
25th November 2005

Contact Details
✉ graduates@lloydstsb.co.uk

Turn to page 192 now to request more information about Lloyds TSB.

The Lloyds TSB Group is one of the UK's leading financial services organisations. Offering a range of products as diverse as personal and corporate banking, mortgages, insurance, investments and pensions, the Lloyds TSB, Scottish Widows and Cheltenham & Gloucester brands are recognised and trusted by millions.

Lloyds TSB's business reaches much further than the High Street. In fact, they employ almost 80,000 people across 20 countries worldwide. Unsurprisingly, the opportunities for graduates are just as diverse. They look for graduates with the ambition and potential to lead their business as a whole. Graduates can join the Group Leadership Programme or on a specialist programme in Finance, linked to the CIMA qualification. Whichever route graduates choose, their training will be tailored to accelerate potential. Lloyds TSB even have their own award-winning corporate university – one of the largest in Europe.

Lloyds TSB will develop leadership potential in a demanding environment – combining formal business-related courses with a series of placements to help graduates become fully-qualified professionals.

Their development will be supported by an experienced Graduate Trainee, a Senior Manager and a Graduate Development Manager. Lloyds TSB will also provide full financial support for relevant professional qualifications.

Lloyds TSB are looking for high academic achievers with energy, initiative and exceptional interpersonal and problem-solving skills. In return, they'll offer graduates an excellent salary, flexible rewards, banking benefits, share options and most importantly, an enjoyable work-life balance.

It's not easy for graduates to choose the right path nowadays. With such a horde of employers looming before you, offering all manner of bright lights and dazzling riches, who could blame you for feeling a bit, well, lost in the dark?

Perhaps you should let us light your way. Because when you open your eyes to Lloyds TSB, you'll see that we're a bit of a dark horse. You'll discover a global business offering private and corporate clients just about every financial service under the sun. You'll find a demanding graduate programme that will make you a leading light in fields as diverse as IT, marketing, accountancy, asset management, risk consultancy, retail and investment banking. Plus you'll throw light on a starting salary upwards of £24,000 and a truly glittering benefits package.

Ready to glow in the dark? For illumination, visit adarkhorse.com

Find your way in the ark

M&S

www.marksandspencer.com/gradcareers

Vacancies for around 100 graduates in 2006

- General Management
- Human Resources
- IT
- Retailing

Starting salary for 2006
£21,000-£24,500

Universities that Marks & Spencer plans to visit in 2005-6

Aston, Bath, Durham, Lancaster, Leeds, London, Manchester, Nottingham, Sheffield, Warwick, York
Please check with your university careers service for details of events.

Application deadline
9th December 2005

Contact Details
Turn to page 192 now to request more information about Marks & Spencer.

Marks & Spencer. A name that has always been associated with quality. Whether it's their much-loved food, clothes and furnishings or the outstanding customer service they provide in their stores, they strive to ensure they always offer the very best. And their graduate scheme is no exception.

It provides the kind of thorough grounding in retail that few other organisations can match. Taking on between two and four placements, over the course of an action-packed 12 months, graduates and business placement students learn about every aspect of the business through a mixture of on-the-job training and expert tuition. Opportunities are divided into two main areas: Stores and Head Office.

From day one, graduates are expected to make real decisions about real issues in the business world. By the end of it, most of their graduates are fully prepared for their first big management role. And that means having substantial responsibilities. Leading a team of people, for example, or running an area of the business worth millions of pounds.

It's easy to see why the M&S graduate scheme is the one everybody wants to get on to. But they look to recruit only the most talented people. People who have the drive and ambition to make the most of all the opportunities on offer. People who can deliver outstanding customer service. And people who can match the energy and vision that have kept M&S at the forefront of the retail industry for so long.

Find out more about everything Marks & Spencer have to offer by visiting www.marksandspencer.com/gradcareers.

Each year, we provide a comprehensive retail training programme to 100 graduates.

And our heartfelt condolences to 1000s more.

● ● ● If only there were a limitless number of vacancies on our graduate scheme. That way everyone could benefit from the unrivalled grounding in retail we provide. Everyone would get to make real decisions from day one. And everyone would be ready, after just 12 months, to take on their first big management role.

As it is, only 100 graduates will get that opportunity. Make sure you're one of them. Visit www.marksandspencer.com/gradcareers to find more.

The graduate scheme everyone wants to get on to.

Mars

The ultimate business school

Enjoy

that

feeling of

inevitable

success.

**Vacancies for around
20-30 graduates in 2006**

- Engineering
- Finance
- General Management
- Marketing
- Research & Development
- Sales

Starting salary for 2006
£25,000

**Universities that
Mars Incorporated
plans to visit in 2005-6**

Bath, Birmingham,
Cambridge, Durham,
Edinburgh, Glasgow,
London, Manchester,
Newcastle, Nottingham,
Oxford, St Andrews,
Strathclyde, Warwick, York.
Please check with your university
careers service for details of events.

Application deadline
27th January 2006

Contact Details

✉ mars.graduate@
eu.effem.co.uk
Turn to page 192 now to request more
information about Mars Incorporated.

Mars, Uncle Ben's, Snickers, Whiskas, M&M's, Dolmio, Twix, Pedigree, Maltesers… these are just some of the household name brands that form the global, $14 billion Mars portfolio. It's little wonder then that it takes 30,000 associates on 140 sites in 60 countries to run a business on this scale. It will also come as no surprise that when recruiting graduates, Mars settles only for the highest calibre.

Surprisingly, Mars Incorporated is still a private, family-owned business. They invest only their own profits in developing the organisation. This means that their graduates – razor sharp business-leaders-in-the-making – get to take more educated risks, explore more avenues and achieve more of everything.

Mars offers development programmes for those who want to specialise in finance, marketing, sales or R&D. These programmes allow graduates to expand their knowledge, stretch their talent and discover a wealth of new skills. Graduates will have access to Mars' tailored training curriculum covering topics such as presentation, leadership and people management skills. Mars supports all its graduates to achieve professional qualifications with financial sponsorship and study leave. Also, the organisation offers a one-year industrial placement for students looking to complement their degree with challenging work experience.

If that wasn't enough, there's the grand prix of graduate schemes – the Mars Management Development Programme. This is a three-year fast-track for the best graduate talent, the opportunity to gain unparalleled experience across all areas of the business, and a platform for a career with no limits.

Mars
The ultimate business school

Stay

You've already proved yourself at university — whether you've finished it yet or not. Now it's time to turn academic excellence few can match into career success that few will emulate. Visit www.mars.com/ultimategrads

a cut

above.

i'm lovin' it

Vacancies for around 100 graduates in 2006

- General Management
- Retailing

Starting salary for 2006
£18,500-£21,500

Universities McDonald's plans to visit in 2005-6
Please check with your university careers service for details of events.

Application deadline
Year-round recruitment

Contact Details
✉ managementrecruitment@uk.mcd.com
☎ 020 8700 7007

Turn to page 192 now to request more information about McDonald's.

fiction you'll spend all your time making burgers not decisions.

Forget the myths that surround working at McDonald's. The facts are far more interesting. McDonald's is one of the world's few truly global brands, with more than 70,000 people in this country and over 1,200 restaurants.

As many of these restaurants have £ million plus turnovers and teams of 60 or more, running one of them is commercial management in its fullest sense. Trainee Business Managers are trained to take on this responsibility through an intensive 19-week management development programme.

The aim is that within two or three years of joining McDonald's graduates will have progressed to Restaurant Manager, which will be like running their own business. As such, they'll set targets, plan budgets, control stock, recruit and train their team, create marketing campaigns and build bridges with the local community.

First, they'll complete a programme that will give hands-on experience of operations, plus expertise in finance, marketing and HR. Graduates will prove themselves at every stage as they progress through 2nd and 1st Assistant Manager to Restaurant Manager and beyond. Shine, and in time they could become an Operations Consultant, controlling a £ multi-million network of restaurants and earning over £50,000.

Long before that, though, graduates will have discovered that good managers are the restaurants' engines. They'll have seen their energy, ideas and hard work influence McDonald's success. And, perhaps most satisfyingly, they'll have shaped a world-leading brand by setting the tone of a restaurant and bringing the best out of their team.

fiction

graduates with big ambitions have no place at McDonald's.

A management career at McDonald's will surprise you. The prospects and rewards are better than most people ever imagine. Within a few years of joining, you could be managing your own restaurant, leading a team of 60, controlling a £multi-million budget and earning a £50k package. First, though, you'll benefit from a comprehensive training programme that will make the most of your degree, initiative and leadership talents. So forget the myths and find out the facts about joining us as a **Trainee Business Manager** on **£18,500 to £21,500***. Apply online at www.mcdonalds.co.uk or call our recruitment hotline on 020 8700 7007.

*dependent on location.

fact in two years' time you could be running a £1million business.

Every one tells a story

INVESTOR IN PEOPLE

MERCER
Human Resource Consulting

www.mercerhr.com/ukgrads

Vacancies for around 80 graduates in 2006

Consulting

Finance

Starting salary for 2006
Up to £26,000

Universities that Mercer HR Consulting Ltd plans to visit in 2005-6

Belfast, Birmingham, Bristol, Cambridge, Durham, Glasgow, Leeds, Liverpool, London, Manchester, Nottingham, Sheffield, St Andrews, Warwick. Please check with your university careers service for details of events.

Application deadline
Year-round recruitment

Contact Details

✉ graduates@mercer.com

☎ 0845 600 2389

Turn to page 192 now to request more information about Mercer HR Consulting Ltd.

Mercer Human Resource Consulting Ltd is one of the largest consultancies of its kind in the world, working with some of the biggest multinational corporations to enhance what it offers its workforce.

Graduate roles focus firmly on all aspects of employee benefits including investment and pension management. The jobs are demanding, intellectually stimulating and will enable graduates to build a career in a global business.

In the Retirement business graduates work with colleagues to offer advice to companies on their pension schemes and retirement strategy. Meanwhile those graduates joining Mercer Investment Consulting help clients understand their pension funds, find appropriate investment strategies and advise on the structure of pension schemes to ensure clients get the best out of their funds.

These are opportunities for ambitious high-calibre graduates – people who are eager to take responsibility at an early stage, and who will enjoy the challenge of delivering precise, high-quality work under the pressure of tight deadlines, competing priorities and shifting goalposts. Graduates will need a minimum of 300 UCAS points and a 2:1 honours degree (or a 2:2 for Valuation Analysts) in a numerate, semi-numerate or business discipline. Actuarial Trainees must have 'A' level Mathematics at grade B or above (or equivalent).

At the start of the programme, graduates will be assigned a 'buddy' and a performance development adviser who'll help them settle in and assess their goals. Then, graduates will join a specially designed graduate training programme, consisting of a structured combination of hands-on technical tuition, and training on a broad range of consulting and personal skills.

What's so interesting about other people's finances?

ctuaries • Analysts • Consultants

It affects individuals and national economies. It involves £multi-billion investment decisions. And it's constantly changing. The pensions industry is one of the most complex and challenging fields of modern commerce. That's one of the reasons why a career with Mercer is such a rewarding ption for high-calibre graduates. You could be dealing with multinational orporations, helping them find the best solutions to their pension or employee enefit problems and achieving success not just through your numerical kills, but also by earning the trust and respect of individual decision-makers. a short, it gives you a huge variety of interesting challenges to think about. nd you'll do it all with the help of intensive training and support towards rofessional qualifications. If you've got 300 UCAS points and are expecting 2:1 degree in a numerate, semi-numerate or business discipline or, for Valuation Analysts a 2:2), find out more at our website **ww.mercerhr.com/ukgrads** Alternatively, please contact a member f the graduate team on **020 7977 8825**.

lot to think about.

rcer aims to attract and retain the best people regardless of their gender, marital status, ethnic origin, ionality, age, background, disability, sexual orientation or beliefs. All recruitment decisions are made the basis of relevant qualifications, skills, knowledge and experience for the role.

STOR IN PEOPLE

www.mercerhr.com/ukgrads

Marsh & McLennan Companies

Merrill Lynch

www.ml.com/careers/europe

Vacancies for around 120 graduates in 2006

- Finance
- Investment Banking
- IT

Vacancies also available in Europe.

Starting salary for 2006
£Competitive

Universities Merrill Lynch plans to visit in 2005-6
Please check with your university careers service for details of events.

Application deadline
See website for full details.

Contact Details

✉ graduate_recruitment
@ml.com

☎ 020 7996 3528

Turn to page 192 now to request more information about Merrill Lynch.

Merrill Lynch is a leading financial management and advisory company with a global network of offices across six continents. The firm offers full-time and summer intern programmes in Global Markets, Investment Banking, Investment Management, Research, Operations and Technology.

At Merrill Lynch, teams of talented and dedicated people work together to achieve the client's objectives. Whether it involves structuring a deal, working on the frontline of customer service, making a trade, or creating tomorrow's e-commerce application, people learn, grow and build on their potential. There is a non-hierarchical approach so employees learn by working side by side with some of the top performers in the business. Employees are encouraged to take on the tougher challenges – and are fully supported in their efforts to achieve success.

Merrill Lynch looks for entrepreneurial individuals with strong commercial acumen. They must be focused in their pursuit of a career in the financial services industry, natural team players and results driven. Relevant work experience and fluency in foreign languages are also positive advantages.

The summer intern experience at Merrill Lynch offers students formal and informal training from industry experts and exposure to the work and culture of the organisation. The ten week programme gives interns the ideal opportunity to prove themselves on the job and, if successful, to receive a full-time offer before graduation. Merrill Lynch also offers a number of off-cycle internships in London, Frankfurt, Madrid, Paris and Milan.

Applications for all positions are accepted online from September.

ml.com/careers/europe

SATISFACTION IS GOOD
PRIDE IS BETTER

Join Merrill Lynch and share in the sense of pride that runs through our organisation. As one of the world's leading financial services firms, we offer our clients all the advantages of a quality brand, as well as continued leadership in products, services and innovation.

This is your opportunity to work alongside some of the sharpest minds in the business. It's a dynamic environment where your mental ability and agility will be constantly tested. Our performance-based culture will reward you for your achievements. However it's not about going it alone. This is a supportive, team-oriented environment where you'll be encouraged to achieve your full potential. If you're accepted onto our summer intern programme, you can expect to be fully involved and make a difference from day one.

There has never been a better time to join Merrill Lynch. We invite you to share in our passion for exceptional performance, while working at the cutting edge of a fast moving industry.

SUMMER INTERN AND FULL-TIME OPPORTUNITIES IN THE FOLLOWING AREAS:

GLOBAL MARKETS

INVESTMENT BANKING

INVESTMENT MANAGEMENT

RESEARCH

OPERATIONS

TECHNOLOGY

For more information or to apply on-line please visit ml.com/careers/europe
Closing date for full-time opportunities: Sunday 6 November 2005 and summer interns: Sunday 15 January 2006.

Merrill Lynch is an equal opportunity employer.

EXCEPTIONAL *WITHOUT EXCEPTION*

www.metpolicecareers.co.uk

Vacancies for around
TBC graduates in 2006

Other

Starting salary for 2006
£28,383
For Police officers after 18 weeks
initial training.

Universities that the
Metropolitan Police
Service plans to visit
in 2005-6
Please check with your university
careers service for details of events.

Application deadline
Year-round recruitment
See website for full details.

Contact Details
Turn to page 192 now to request
more information about the
Metropolitan Police Service.

The Metropolitan Police Service believe that the eight million or so people who live in London (and the many more who work in and visit our capital city) deserve a police service that properly represents them. A safer London can only be achieved if everyone work's together.

That's why it's essential that graduates have a genuine respect for diversity together with the sensitivity to work effectively with London's many different communities. People from all different backgrounds work for the Met. And they don't just work as Police Officers, but as just about every job title someone can think of, and quite a few others that they can't.

Graduates can choose the career they want. And by career, the Met mean career. That's what graduates get from day one. The Met does not have a specific graduate scheme. However, they have careers that matter and that mean something. What they do offer is a Police Officer Higher Potential Development scheme – graduate or not it's open to everyone. The scheme provides a structured route to some of the most senior positions in the Met. Leadership ability is the key quality and the scheme is designed to identify and enhance management and command skills through tailored training.

If the role of Police Officer is not suitable, consider joining as a member of Police Staff in areas such as marketing, HR, forensics, legal services, IT and finance – the list is endless.

Whatever career graduates choose with the Met, they offer highly competitive salaries and packages to all their staff. And then, of course, there are the other rewards. Around eight million of them, in fact.

WHAT USE IS YOUR DEGREE TO HIM?

Not a lot. Not if you don't do anything with it. Not if you're more interested in sales figures going up than crime going down.

With your degree you should be able to do just about anything. At the Met you can. We can offer you a range of career paths, from Police Officer to Human Resources, Accountancy to Forensics, IT to Marketing and Communications.

One thing we won't offer you is a career where you sit around for two years watching other people do the work that matters.

No doubt you're thinking hard about what you want to do. Imagine what you could do if you really wanted.

Your degree's worth a lot. So are you. Find out how much by going to

www.metpolicecareers.co.uk/grad

We particularly welcome applications from students from under-represented communities.

MI5
THE SECURITY SERVICE

www.mi5careers.co.uk

Vacancies for around 35 graduates in 2006

- General Management
- IT
- Research & Development

Starting salary for 2006
£Competitive

Universities that MI5 plans to visit in 2005-6
Please check with your university careers service for details of events.

Application deadline
Varies by function
See website for full details.

Contact Details
Turn to page 192 now to request more information about MI5.

MI5 is the UK's security intelligence agency, protecting the nation's people, economy and institutions from threats such as terrorism, espionage and serious crime.

Desk Officers join MI5 from any degree discipline. During a career a Desk Officer is likely to carry out a range of jobs such as assessing and investigating threats to national security, financial and HR management or operational work such as recruiting and running agents.

Graduates can also join as linguists, listening to and translating a variety of communications in a particular language, whether it is mother tongue or formally studied. Key languages include Sorani, Arabic (including North African), Bengali and Urdu.

Technically astute graduates can apply for a variety of IT positions, including providing 1st and 2nd line systems support and network security work and advice. Some experience is preferable, as is a computer-related degree or HND. A team of electronics and laboratory technicians supports the Service's technical requirements in a number of disciplines. Flexible candidates with a C&G or relevant degree (depending on the position) might join MI5 in the scientific or technical departments.

To apply it is necessary to be a British Citizen. Further details about these roles, nationality and residency requirements can be found on the website. Please be aware that the recruitment and vetting process can take up to eight months. Discretion is important to the Service, so candidates are asked only to discuss their application with close family and/or partner. More information is available on the website (www.mi5careers.co.uk).

HOW DO WE USE OUR INTELLIGENCE? IN OVER 30 TYPES OF CAREER.

Microsoft®

www.microsoft.com/uk/graduates

Vacancies for around 30 graduates in 2006

- Consulting
- Finance
- General Management
- IT
- Marketing
- Research & Development
- Sales

Starting salary for 2006
£23,500
Plus a sign-on bonus.

Universities Microsoft plans to visit in 2005-6

Aston, Bath, Birmingham, Brunel, Cambridge, Kent, Lancaster, Loughborough, London, Manchester, Nottingham, Nottingham Trent, Oxford, Reading, Sheffield, Warwick.
Please check with your university careers service for details of events.

Application deadline
31st December 2005

Contact Details

✉ gradrec@microsoft.com

Turn to page 192 now to request more information about Microsoft.

Microsoft has deliberately created an environment where great people can do their best. Hard work is expected, but graduates are free to satisfy their intellectual curiosity.

For example, their Reading campus is somewhere people can think along new lines, explore truly exciting technology and enjoy spending time. Microsoft recognises employees have a life outside the campus. Their reasoning is that people aren't machines, and need intellectual and emotional space.

Their approach to training and development is equally refreshing. Microsoft helps to identify strengths and encourages graduates to play to them. They believe that when people are doing what they're good at, they enjoy themselves and they do it better. In other words, what makes individuals different is what makes them outstanding.

The people who flourish there are natural communicators with inquisitive natures, a passion for technology and an instinctive understanding of customers. But what really sets them apart is a drive that raises them above the average whether they join commercial or technical business groups.

The graduate programme includes residential courses at international locations and self-directed learning. Involvement in real projects gives graduates real responsibility, while mentors advise throughout. The basic requirements are a 2:1, creativity, vision, people skills, an inquiring mind and a willingness to learn.

The emphasis during student placements in Reading or London is on supplementing theory learnt at university with real, practical experience. The 48-week scheme starts in July with a week-long induction. Training can include residential courses and self-directed learning.

Curiosity never killed a graduate.

Not at Microsoft anyway. Here, it's positively life (and career) enhancing. Our company relies on questioning, investigating and generally being nosy in order to advance.

As a graduate recruit you'll have to tackle uncharted territory, whether you're working in **Technical, Sales** or **Marketing**. It might mean discovering how others work or thinking along new lines. Either way, you'll be stepping outside your comfort zone. In fact, you'll be exploring new territory not just when you arrive, but throughout your career, because it's part of our culture to try new things and seek innovation.

To find out more and to apply go to **www.microsoft.com/uk/graduates**

Satisfy your curiosity

Microsoft
Your potential. Our passion.

MᵒD→RECRUITMENT

www.mod.uk

Vacancies for around 100 graduates in 2006

- Engineering
- Finance
- General Management
- IT
- Logistics

Starting salary for 2006
£Competitive

Universities that the MOD plans to visit in 2005-6
Please check with your university careers service for details of events.

Application deadline
Year-round recruitment

Contact Details
Turn to page 192 now to request more information about the MOD.

A career within the Ministry of Defence (MOD) provides a unique opportunity to work at the heart of UK Government in an organisation that has international influence. The 70,000 Civilians in the MOD are employed to support the Armed Forces, including formulation of defence policy and advice to senior Military officers and Ministers.

The MOD is looking for people who take the lead in any situation and will build solid working relationships, whatever their discipline, background or culture. It needs effective communicators, people who can demonstrate organisational skills, creativity and intellect. In return, graduates can expect personal and professional development and high-quality ongoing training opportunities (often leading to the achievement of a professional qualification).

The MOD recognises talent, and provides more rapid development opportunities for the most talented. The MOD also offers opportunities to work abroad, flexible working patterns, a good maternity package and career break options. Equality of opportunity is paramount, and the MOD is taking active steps to increase representation of women, people from ethnic-minority backgrounds and people with disabilities.

MOD Civilians are part of the wider Civil Service and are subject to the legal requirements governing Civil Service recruitment. Engineering & science undergraduates and graduates should visit the Defence Engineering & Science Group (DESG) website at www.desg.mod.uk. Most posts are open to UK and Irish nationals, Commonwealth citizens and certain non-European Economic Area family members.

ALL THE DIRECTION YOU NEED.

Unparalleled opportunities for personal and professional development

Locations throughout the UK and overseas, from Project Management at the forefront of technology to Personnel Management and Training

Lots of scope to move internally

Civilians in the Ministry of Defence provide crucial equipment and support to the British Armed Forces, helping in their goal of strengthening international peace and security.

As British Industry's largest single customer, the MOD spends around £10 billion a year on equipment, support and services; and it's important we spend it well. To do that, we rely on recruiting and retaining the very best people from all parts of society.

Every opportunity to find the right career
Our graduate and other programmes are designed to be flexible, so you can move job and location or change career direction if you want to, whilst retaining your status and similar working conditions. This means you can embark on a new career path or choose to study for professional qualifications, whilst continuing your pension and annual leave allowances.

Choice of career paths
Engineering and Science
Project Management
Commercial Officers/Purchasing
Finance
Linguists, Statistician and Medical Staff
Logisticians
Human Resources
Training and Development
Policy
Information Technology

For specific vacancies, see: **www.mod.uk**

MoD→RECRUITMENT

MINISTRY OF DEFENCE

The MOD is an equal opportunity employer aiming for the widest possible diversity in its workforce, drawing recruits from every part of the community. We particularly welcome applications from ethnic minority people, women and people with disabilities who are currently under-represented in the MOD.

Morgan Stanley

www.morganstanley.com/careers/recruiting

Vacancies for around 150 graduates in 2006

- Finance
- Investment Banking
- IT

Starting salary for 2006
£Competitive

Universities that Morgan Stanley plans to visit in 2005-6

Bath, Bristol, Cambridge, Dublin, Edinburgh, Glasgow, London, Manchester, Oxford, Southampton, St Andrews, Warwick, York.
Please check with your university careers service for details of events.

Application deadline
16th November 2005

Contact Details

☎ 020 7425 8000
Turn to page 192 now to request more information about Morgan Stanley.

Morgan Stanley is one of the best-known names in financial services: a leader in connecting people, ideas and capital to help clients achieve their financial aspirations.

The firm has earned a worldwide reputation for the excellence of its advice and execution in financial markets. They serve institutional and individual investors and investment banking clients, around the world. Truly global, the firm is a market leader in Europe and Asia as well as the United States: their 53,000 employees work in 600 offices in 28 countries.

Morgan Stanley nurtures an atmosphere that is team-oriented and collegial: its people respect each other and enjoy working closely together in a structure that is less hierarchical than that of many of its competitors. Within their culture of mutual respect, Morgan Stanley is known as a company where individuality is prized and people are encouraged to be themselves, with diverse backgrounds and personal interests.

Analyst training at Morgan Stanley quickly makes effective professionals. Through a structured programme, graduates receive an intensive induction on how to use Morgan Stanley's unsurpassed data resources and analytic tools.

Graduates work on a team under the direct guidance of senior professionals who are among the best in their fields. They will give as much responsibility as graduates can handle, in a dynamic environment that affords exciting opportunities to work with a wide variety of clients in different industries, helping them to make strategic decisions involving capital raising, research or trading issues at the highest level. Training is not limited to the first weeks or months on the job but is ongoing throughout a career at Morgan Stanley.

Morgan Stanley

Are you Morgan Stanley?

E INVITE YOU TO FIND OUT.

rgan Stanley is a global community dedicated to achievement. We help corporations, governments and others to solve the
st complex problems in finance, including restructuring, mergers and acquisitions, and privatisations. From conference room
rading floor, we can show you a career from different angles. And we'll put you side by side with the best in the business –
ple who challenge your thinking and who listen when you challenge theirs.

und interesting? Then Morgan Stanley might just be the right place for you.

SIT AND APPLY ONLINE AT WWW.MORGANSTANLEY.COM/CAREERS

an Stanley is an equal opportunity/affirmative action employer committed to workforce diversity. (M/F/D/V) © 2005 Morgan Stanley

ngdp

FOR LOCAL GOVERNMENT

www.ngdp.co.uk

Vacancies for around 100 graduates in 2006

General Management

Starting salary for 2006
£22,000
Plus London weighting.

Universities that ngdp plans to visit in 2005-6
Birmingham, Bristol, Cambridge, Durham, Leeds, London, Manchester, Nottingham, Oxford, Sheffield, Warwick.
Please check with your university careers service for details of events.

Application deadline
6th January 2006

Contact Details

✉ enquiry@ngdp.co.uk
☎ 0845 222 0250

Turn to page 192 now to request more information about ngdp.

The ngdp is a two-year graduate development programme designed to develop future managers and leaders in local government. It was set up to provide local government with the high calibre managers their communities need and to give committed graduates the training, qualifications and opportunities to make a real difference.

Local government is the largest employer in the UK, with over 2 million staff in over 400 local authorities and in excess of 500 different occupational areas. These include some that graduates may expect a local authority or council to provide, for example social workers, and many that graduates may not, for instance business analysts, consultants and solicitors.

Local government is going through many positive changes at present, and as a trainee on the ngdp graduates will be at the forefront of these changes.

The programme consists of placements in key areas of local authority service. Every participating authority will offer a unique experience, within set national guidelines, and the work is generally high level and management orientated.

The placements will offer a range of experiences designed to provide a broad understanding of many aspects of local government including: strategy, service delivery and support service.

National training includes study for the postgraduate diploma in local government management, and residential events designed to develop skills. Peer development is also encouraged. Further training and development will be available through the employing authority.

NATIONAL GRADUATE
DEVELOPMENT PROGRAMME

ngdp.
FOR LOCAL GOVERNMENT

REAL
CONCERNS

Crystal Clear Acrylic Coating

Working for local government isn't about dynamic business deals or long lunches. It's about something far more remarkable: delivering real solutions for real communities with real problems. It could see you tackling anti-social behaviour or racism. Equally, it could be about helping a local authority work more efficiently and effectively. Whatever challenges you face, the issues will be complex, difficult and most of all important.

The **ngdp** is a graduate development programme designed to provide local government with the high calibre managers their communities need, and give committed graduates the training, qualifications and opportunities to make a real difference. Over two years you'll undertake a series of placements, covering front line services, support services and strategy. You'll receive a competitive salary and benefits, and excellent personal and professional development opportunities. Most of all, you'll get the chance to see your ideas have real impact. To find out more, visit **www.ngdp.co.uk** or call **0845 222 0250** for a brochure.

Real life. Real work.

www.ngdp.co.uk

NHS

www.bringingleadershiptolife.nhs.uk

The National Health Service is the largest employer in Europe. With over one million staff and a £67 billion budget, they offer an ideal training ground for a career at the leading edge of public sector management. Currently undergoing the largest change management programme ever conducted, their aim is to transform the service into a modern, efficient organisation, ready to meet the challenge of 21st century health needs.

Right now, the NHS are looking for intelligent, imaginative, creative thinkers with sheer leadership ability – people with the drive to deliver tremendously complex services, whilst actively challenging and developing the way the NHS does things. They offer three highly acclaimed, tailored training programmes; Financial Management, General Management and Human Resources Management, across England and Wales – all designed to train, develop and nurture future Directors and Chief Executives.

Management in the NHS is not a soft option and the selection processes are stretching to say the least. They have to be, because NHS managers today are dealing with issues, concepts and demands that require the most enlightened, innovative and expert thinking. It will be challenging but the pressures of the role are more than matched by the rewards.

Progress can be rapid and it's entirely possible to reach Director level in a major NHS organisation within five years of completing your scheme. What's more, the results of your work can change people's lives.

For further information about the Schemes and to apply, please visit www.bringingleadershiptolife.nhs.uk.

You don't have to be an audiologist to listen.

Graduate Schemes – Financial, General and HR

It doesn't take hi-tech equipment to make a difference to people's lives. Join the NHS Graduate Training Schemes and you'll enjoy the chance to deliver effective management solutions that do just as much to ensure patients receive the highest quality care.

Whether your future lies in Finance, HR or General management, our Graduate Schemes offer the chance to gain qualifications while working alongside experienced professionals. It won't be easy. We're looking for people with the passion, drive and determination to make a difference. If you have at least a 2:2 degree in any subject and a hard work ethic that will guarantee results, visit our website or call 0870 169 9731 to find out more.

www.bringingleadershiptolife.nhs.uk

NHS

Bringing leadership to life

Oxfam

www.oxfam.org.uk/what_you_can_do/volunteer/internship.htm

Vacancies for around 60 graduates in 2006

- Accountancy
- Finance
- General Management
- Human Resources
- IT
- Marketing
- Media
- Research & Development
- Retailing

Starting salary for 2006
£Voluntary

Universities that Oxfam plans to visit in 2005-6
Please check with your university careers service for details of events.

Application deadline
Year-round recruitment

Contact Details
✉ internship@oxfam.org.uk
Turn to page 192 now to request more information about Oxfam.

Oxfam is a development, relief, and campaigning organisation which is working towards a world without poverty.

Oxfam is about people, and people are its greatest resource: over 20,000 volunteers help run Oxfam's famous high street shops; over 500,000 individuals make regular donations; more than a million people worldwide support its campaigns; and countless individuals in more than 80 countries work their own way out of poverty, with Oxfam's support.

Oxfam is looking for committed, enthusiastic people to take part in its voluntary Internship Scheme. For those who are passionate about the work and high values of Oxfam, and are willing to take on responsibility in this high-profile, professional charity, this could be an ideal opportunity. Interns may expect to develop campaigns, trial new ideas, promote policies, work on projects, carry out research, manage an Oxfam shop, plan Oxfam events and much more!

The Oxfam Internship Scheme is divided into three intakes throughout the year – January to May, June to August and September to December. Although it is unpaid, the new scheme provides an allowance for lunch and travel expenses, and the flexible hours will enable participants to get part-time jobs to finance their internship. Most Oxfam Internship opportunities are based in the Oxford Head Office, though there are also opportunities in Oxfam's other UK offices and in their nationwide shop network.

If you have what it takes to inspire others to change the world, there's no better place to do it. For more information please visit Oxfam's Internship Scheme website.

ooking for a volunteer internship where ou can really make a difference?

You get experience and skills in a unique nvironment with a charity striving o overcome poverty.

We get the benefit of your energy nd enthusiasm.

Change starts here…

ww.oxfam.org.uk/what_you_can_do/volunteer/internship.htm

liver the promises'
(Hindi)

'No more poverty'
(Hindi)

Oxfam works with others
to overcome poverty and suffering

Oxfam GB is a member of Oxfam International.
Registered charity no. 202918

Oxfam

PA Consulting Group

www.paconsulting.com

Vacancies for around 40 graduates in 2006

- Consulting
- Engineering
- Finance
- IT
- Research & Development

Starting salary for 2005
£32,000
Plus performance-related bonus.

Universities that PA plans to visit in 2005-6
Aston, Bath, Birmingham, Cambridge, Cardiff, Lancaster, London, Loughborough, Manchester, Nottingham, Oxford, Strathclyde, Warwick.
Please check with your university careers service for details of events.

Application deadline
31st March 2006

Contact Details
✉ graduaterecruitment@
         paconsulting.com
Turn to page 192 now to request more information about PA Consulting.

PA Consulting Group is a leading management, systems and technology consulting firm. Operating worldwide in more than 35 countries, PA draws on the knowledge and experience of 3,000 people.

PA is looking to recruit graduates into: IT, Decision Sciences, Industry areas (Government Services, Financial Services, Energy), Business Operations & Performance, Applied Technology, and Strategy & Marketing. Relevant work experience is desirable for all areas. An excellent academic record is essential (minimum 24 UCAS points; 2:1 degree), as is the ability to work co-operatively with others, and to present ideas effectively and persuasively. Graduates will also need a high degree of drive and tenacity in order to achieve their goals. Ambition and business acumen are vital.

All graduates attend a four week training programme. The programme covers essential aspects of business, consulting and interpersonal skills. Optional courses enhance technical and non-technical skills and knowledge. PA will provide graduates with on-going training as well as on-the-job learning.

Graduates will follow a career path which sets out levels of experience, achievement and personal competence so that, at every stage of their career, they know exactly what is required of them to progress. Graduates will be given advice and encouragement to help them develop (they will be given support from their individual line manager and mentor), but it remains a graduate's personal responsibility to ensure that they continue to grow, not just in their first few years but also for the rest of their career with PA.

For more information, please visit the PA web site.

PA Consulting Group

Look
closer...

Not all consulting firms are the same. PA Consulting Group works across the full spectrum of management, systems and technology consulting – operating worldwide in more than 35 countries and drawing on the knowledge and experience of 3,000 people.

PA will offer you a challenging career path, with opportunities for you to progress, as you acquire new skills and experience. We give excellent training in a supportive environment, which will provide you with the tools to develop yourself to your fullest potential. Everyone has the opportunity to earn equity in the firm, so we all think and act as owners, not just as employees.

We've attained many awards in recent years, visit http://www.paconsulting.com/news/award_winning_work for details.

For more information on graduate careers at PA, take a closer look at our Web site.

PA is an equal opportunity employer.

We recognise that diversity is strength and that the differences between people add value to our organisation. PA Consulting Group is committed to equality and diversity and positively welcomes applications from suitably qualified candidates from all backgrounds, regardless of sex, sexual orientation, disability, ethnicity, religion or age.

Look closer @
www.paconsulting.com

COULD YOU?
POLICE

www.policecouldyou.co.uk

Vacancies for unlimited **graduates in 2006**

■ Other

Starting salary for 2006
£19,803
After intial training period.

Universities that HPD plans to visit in 2005-6
Bath, Belfast, Birmingham, Brunel, Cardiff, Durham, East Anglia, Essex, Hull, Lancaster, Liverpool, London, Manchester, Newcastle, Northumbria, Nottingham, Nottingham Trent, Oxford, Sheffield, Sussex, Warwick, York
Please check with your university careers service for details of events.

Application deadline
Year-round recruitment

Contact Details
☎ 020 7035 5050
Turn to page 192 now to request more information about HPD.

The Police Service offers a career that is exciting, stimulating and rewarding. In today's modern Police Service graduates can help to reduce crime and the fear of crime. Policing offers the opportunity to work in partnership with the public and other organisations and make a real difference to the community.

Graduates are important in the Police Service and the High Potential Development scheme (HPD) welcomes graduates who have the qualities for the challenges of current policing. HPD has been designed to support and develop future leaders of the Police Service, to improve their leadership and command skills and assist them to progress to senior positions.

The scheme aims to turn potential into performance, whether as a highly effective middle manager in command and leadership roles, or beyond that at the strategic leadership level of the service. The scheme provides successful applicants with a range of career opportunities, rewarding those who have the vision, drive and determination to face the challenges before them.

HPD offers a structured career development programme with an emphasis on self-development. Applicants are encouraged to pursue specific areas of interest and to broaden their career horizons.

As part of the scheme all successful applicants will have a higher education opportunity. There are many options available, dependent on their career aspirations, drive and determination to succeed within the Police Service. Sponsorship up to £6,000 is available, though scheme members must demonstrate that the chosen course of study is relevant to their own individual career development, and to the Police Service.

Could you turn
your potential
into performance?

The High Potential Development (HPD) scheme has been designed to support and develop the future leaders of the Police service, to improve their leadership and command skills, and assist them to progress to senior positions.

The scheme encourages individuals to fulfil their own expectations, pursue specific areas of interest and broaden their horizons. The greater the effort, commitment and initiative of the applicant, the greater the prospective rewards.

The High Potential Development scheme
Exceptional opportunities for exceptional graduates

To go forward, call 020 7035 5050
or visit www.policecouldyou.co.uk

PRICEWATERHOUSECOOPERS

www.pwc.com/uk/careers/

Vacancies for around
1,200 graduates in 2006

- Accountancy
- Consulting
- Finance
- Law

Starting salary for 2006
£Competitive
Plus flexible benefits and an
interest-free loan.

Universities that
PricewaterhouseCoopers
plans to visit in 2005-6
Please check with your university
careers service for details of events.

Application deadline
Varies by function
See website for full details.

Contact Details
☎ 0808 100 1500 /
+44 (0)121 265 5852

Turn to page 192 now to request
more information about
PricewaterhouseCoopers.

Graduates will probably have heard of PricewaterhouseCoopers LLP (PwC), but may not know exactly what they do. As a large professional services firm, their work is hugely diverse.

With offices all over the world, they work with an enormous range of clients – businesses, charities and governments – providing services that help to improve the way they work in the short and long-term. From auditing their finances and planning their taxes to identifying the commercial risks they face and assessing the implications of strategic decisions, PwC work in partnership with all their clients creating leading-edge solutions.

All in all, PwC offers talented graduates a great introduction to the world of business in a supportive and team-oriented environment. And with a range of business groups to choose from, they have something to offer everyone, whatever the subject of their degree and wherever their interests lie. Indeed, they're looking for high-calibre graduates with the thirst and enthusiasm to build a successful career in business.

Whether graduates join the Assurance, Advisory or Tax group, they will study towards a professional qualification which will combine on-the-job training with study. So, graduates will need to be prepared to work hard from day one.

PwC's supportive culture will give graduates everything they need to excel, which is all part of their investment in their people and continuous professional development.

Across the UK their positions fill up quickly each year so early application is advised. To find out more about opportunities available for graduates at PricewaterhouseCoopers, visit www.pwc.com/uk/careers/

You'd be surprised
what we get up to...

Graduate Opportunities Nationwide – Autumn 2006

ot everyone realises the sheer breadth of activities we et involved in at PricewaterhouseCoopers. In fact we fer an enormous range of services, from providing ersonal tax for high net-worth (and extremely high 'ofile) clients to overseeing the voting for the Oscars. nd that's just entertainment – one of the multitude industry sectors we cover. But that's not the only rprise you'll find here.

nother big surprise is that careers at PwC are about uch more than simply number-crunching. Whether e're auditing a company's financial results, identifying e commercial risks they face, helping with tax anning or assessing the implications of strategic ısiness decisions – it's about getting beneath the skin other organisations*. So wherever you join us, you'll

be dealing directly with clients right from the start, while working towards a professional qualification. And since the challenges we face span virtually every industry sector, the depth and breadth of experience you'll gain will equip you for an exciting career.

Even more surprising, you don't need a business or finance degree to join us. Yes, you've got to be comfortable dealing with numbers and you must have a strong academic record. But the subject of your degree is less important than your willingness to contribute and your eagerness to learn.

Find out more at **www.pwc.com/uk/careers/**

Go on, surprise yourself.

connectedthinking

*P*RICE*WATERHOUSE*C*OOPERS*

P&G

Vacancies for around 100 graduates in 2006

- Engineering
- Finance
- Human Resources
- IT
- Logistics
- Marketing
- Purchasing
- Research & Development
- Sales

Starting salary for 2006
£27,000

Universities that Procter & Gamble plans to visit in 2005-6

Bath, Birmingham, Cambridge, Dublin, Durham, Edinburgh, Leeds, London, Manchester, Newcastle, Nottingham, Oxford, Sheffield, Strathclyde, Warwick.
Please check with your university careers service for details of events.

Application deadline
See website for full details.

Contact Details

 recunitedkingdm.im@pg.com

☎ 0800 056 5258/
+44 870 900 5013
Turn to page 192 now to request more information about Procter & Gamble.

Two billion times a day, P&G brands touch the lives of people around the world. They have one of the largest and strongest portfolios of trusted, quality brands, including Pampers, Ariel, Always, Pantene, Pringles and Olay. Nearly 98,000 P&G people working in 80 countries worldwide make sure P&G brands live up to their promise to make everyday life just a little better.

Their purpose: to provide branded products and services of superior quality and value that improve the lives of the world's consumers. As a result, consumers will reward them with leadership sales, profit and value creation, allowing their people, their shareholders and the communities in which they live and work to prosper.

P&G People: they continue to attract and recruit the finest people in the world, because it is people who determine the long-term success of Procter & Gamble: they are the company's biggest asset and the guardians of their purpose, values and principles.

The people first culture encourages individuals from every nationality, race and background to create brilliant solutions together. They recruit individualists: lateral thinkers. The sort of free spirit they seek is determined to take early responsibility, make a significant difference, and fulfil their potential.

Graduates can count on P&G to give the support and guidance they need to achieve bold ambitions. At the same time, they'll be honest about performance. They'll help to calculate risk and to measure it against the long-term gains to their business.

their fun is your challenge

Pringles is one of our most loved brands in the world. The secret of its success could be many things – great flavours, unique packaging or its fun advertising. In fact, the reason for Pringles success is simple – it's all down to the diverse teams that work on the brand at Procter & Gamble. People will always be our most important asset.

We are looking for people who are ready to face diverse challenges and get a real buzz from overcoming them to achieve great results. For those who are passionate about innovating and resolute about winning and improving the lives of consumers worldwide.

Ready for your challenge ? Then we are ready for you. We will give you the best training, mentoring and support to help you succeed. Please visit our careers site www.pgcareers.com.

a new challenge every day   www. *PG careers* .com

Procter & Gamble is a fast moving consumer goods company with opportunities in Finance, IT, Customer Business Development (Sales), Human Resources, Product Supply, Research and Development and Marketing. We offer full time and internship positions in all the above functions and accept applications from all fields of study (except for Research & Development and Product Supply where specific degrees are required).

QinetiQ

www.QinetiQ.com/careers

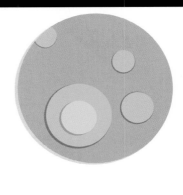

Vacancies for around 300 graduates in 2006

- Engineering
- General Management
- IT
- Research & Development

Starting salary for 2006
£23,000

Universities that QinetiQ plans to visit in 2005-6
Bath, Birmingham, Bristol, Exeter, Liverpool, London, Loughborough, Oxford, Southampton, St Andrews, Surrey.
Please check with your university careers service for details of events.

Application deadline
Year-round recruitment

Contact Details
Turn to page 192 now to request more information about QinetiQ.

V
is for venus-bound microsatellites

QinetiQ makes the world's most complex problems look simple. Combining the intelligence, imagination and energy of some of the world's leading research scientists, they make the impossible an everyday reality.

A world-renowned defence and security technology company, QinetiQ delivers commercial value from science. That means taking the forward thinking required in the defence world and bringing it to the widest possible range of civil projects. They offer a similarly broad range of careers covering operational analysis, scientific research, development, test and evaluation and project management – in fields ranging from media to healthcare, aerospace to security and telecoms to transport.

QinetiQ's proud heritage includes inventing the jet engine, thermal imaging, flat panel speakers and carbon fibre. No wonder they're a world leader in the creation and application of technology. QinetiQ seeks around 300 extraordinary new people a year. They look for analytical, forward-thinking graduates from most science, engineering, IT and numerate disciplines. They offer a good salary and benefits package combined with real quality of life.

QinetiQ give their people the freedom, resources and training they need to push the boundaries of existing knowledge and inspire one another. They also offer the chance to work alongside some of the leading people in their field.

In addition to our core graduate development programme there is the potential to attend conferences, undertake secondments and, where appropriate, support for further qualifications, such as Chartered status, an MSc, or PhD.

Whatever route graduates take, they will be surrounded by opportunities.

q

is for *QinetiQ*

Q is for questioning everything. Q is for QED. Q is for quasars, quicksilver and quantum cryptography. Q is for quieter jumbo jets. Q is for Q as in 'Do try to keep up, Bond'. Q is always questing for something better. Q is quintessentially about making complex science and engineering problems look simple. Q is for quality graduates from a huge range of disciplines. Q is for visit **www.QinetiQ.com/careers** quickly.

QinetiQ
we make it look simple

REUTERS ⠿

Vacancies for around 30 graduates in 2006

- Accountancy
- Finance
- General Management
- IT
- Media

Starting salary for 2006
£Competitive

Universities that Reuters plans to visit in 2005-6
Please check with your university careers service for details of events.

Application deadline
31st December 2005

Contact Details
✉ candidate.support@reuters.com

Turn to page 192 now to request more information about Reuters.

Reuters is a leading global provider of news, financial information and technology solutions to financial institutions, the media, corporates and individuals.

Over 15,500 people work for Reuters in 210 cities, in 92 countries and this is probably the most exciting period in Reuters' long history. They strive to break new ground and create new traditions whilst also maintaining their 150-year heritage. Graduates who are stimulated by continual challenge, and who want a career with variety without constantly switching companies, pinpoint Reuters as an employer of choice.

Reuters look for a consistently strong academic track record and at least a 2.1 degree or international equivalent. Other things are important too, such as evidence of mental agility, initiative and tenacity. A healthy interest in the financial markets and web literacy is essential. They offer four graduate programmes and language requirements vary for each.

Reuters' business has many facets, and the programmes expose graduates to as many of them as possible through assignments in different parts of the organisation. Within the first twelve to eighteen months, it is likely that graduates will be working on an international project – gaining experience of Reuters' business.

For individuals with drive and ambition, the graduate programmes provide a platform for creative ideas and limitless scope to make a real impact. Reuters encourage and expect graduates to play a decisive role in defining their own future. But, a word of warning to anyone who likes to deal in absolute certainties: in the Reuters world, there are none.

RUN WITH THE EYES AND EARS OF THE WORLD

The world gets its news from Reuters. No matter where, no matter what, no matter when – we get the story out. Providing indispensable information for the financial services, media and corporate markets, we help drive decision making around the globe.

Accuracy is our first priority. But speed is a close second. Right from our earliest days, we've pioneered the fastest, most innovative technology. Reuters' report of Abraham Lincoln's assassination reached London two hours ahead of any other. We scooped the first interview with the men who conquered Everest in 1953. We were first with news of the Berlin Wall's construction – and, 28 years later, its destruction. Today, in addition to supplying real-time data on 5.5 million financial records from 258 exchanges and over-the-counter markets, we're the most read news source on the Internet. And we publish on average 30,000 headlines and over eight million words in 19 languages, every single day.

Finance, media and technology – it's all here. Together, it all adds up to huge opportunities for the brightest and most ambitious graduates to shape the future of one of the world's great companies.

Visit our website for further details of our four programmes:

- Technology
- European Graduate Programme – Business
- Finance
- Journalism

REUTERS

KNOW NOW

www.reuters.com/careers/graduate

Rolls-Royce

www.rolls-royce.com/university

**Vacancies for around
100 graduates in 2006**

- Engineering
- Finance
- Human Resources
- Logistics
- Purchasing
- Sales

Starting salary for 2006
£23,000+

**Universities Rolls-Royce
plans to visit in 2005-6**

Aston, Belfast, Birmingham,
Bristol, Cambridge, Cardiff,
Dublin, Loughborough,
Manchester, Nottingham,
Oxford, Sheffield,
Southampton, Strathclyde,
Warwick.
Please check with your university
careers service for details of events.

Application deadline
Year-round recruitment

Contact Details

✉ peoplelink@rolls-royce.com

☎ 01332 244344

Turn to page 192 now to request
more information about Rolls-Royce.

Rolls-Royce plc operates in four main markets – civil and defence aerospace, marine and energy, providing gas turbine power for customers all over the globe. With 35,000 employees worldwide, they have main sites in the UK, North America, Germany and the Nordic countries. Although they're best known as an engineering business, they are primarily a business so they're looking for people across a wide range of functions.

Rolls-Royce offers seven different graduate programmes in engineering, finance, logistics, purchasing, operations management, customer relationship management and human resources. Apart from engineering, none of the programmes require specific degrees.

The programme is tailored to meet the needs of the individual graduate, depending on the function they've joined, their own experience, their interests and, of course, the business needs. Although it is a development programme, trainees are expected to contribute to the business from day one and each attachment will come with challenging objectives and real projects.

Rolls-Royce is very strong on professional development and will support graduates to achieve further relevant qualifications and membership of professional institutions. There's also the chance to be involved in education or community projects – a great way for graduates to challenge themselves whilst giving something back.

Rolls-Royce is a truly global company, and many graduates find their development programme includes an international secondment to one of their own sites or to a customer or supplier.

Want to spread your wings?

are a truly international company, a market leader in power neration with a great history and a world famous name. ou're ready to spread your wings, take a look at our ortunities in engineering, finance, purchasing, logistics, human resources, operations management and customer relationship management to see how your career could take off. You could be flying high in no time…

Trusted to deliver excellence

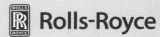 Rolls-Royce

The Royal Bank of Scotland Group

www.rbs.com/graduates

Vacancies for around 200 graduates in 2006

- Accountancy
- Consulting
- Finance
- General Management
- Human Resources
- Investment Banking
- IT
- Retailing
- Sales

Starting salary for 2006
£Competitive

Universities that The Royal Bank of Scotland Group plans to visit in 2005-6

Belfast, Bristol, Cambridge, Dublin, Durham, Edinburgh, Glasgow, Leeds, London, Manchester, Nottingham, Oxford, St Andrews, Strathclyde, Warwick. **Please check with your university careers service for details of events.**

Application deadline
Varies by function
See website for full details.

Contact Details
Turn to page 192 now to request more information about The Royal Bank of Scotland Group.

LIFE IS A SERIES OF DESTINATIONS

There are many different questions that graduates face – what to do, where to go and how to get there. These are probably some of the questions going through their minds at the moment. The Royal Bank of Scotland Group can help find the answers. This is one of the biggest banking groups in the world with more than 40 different brands. In the UK alone, there are market-leading brands such as NatWest, Coutts & Co, Direct Line, Churchill and The Royal Bank of Scotland itself.

Rather than just one graduate programme, there are many. Rather than just one career destination, there are hundreds. Graduates are encouraged to think beyond the graduate programme and see the benefits of working within Europe's second-largest financial institution; which incidentally has more people in North America than it does in Scotland. Such is the range and scope of the opportunities within the different businesses and the Group itself that graduates can build amazing careers within this organisation. The programmes range from corporate banking to retail, from HR to finance. The entry and role requirements for each are different – and it is important to consider carefully, before applying, which programme would suit applicants best.

Development is thorough and individual wherever they go, the reward package is excellent and with the size and breadth of the business, this is a career journey that could take graduates in many different directions, to many different destinations.

Experience the journey and apply at www.rbs.com/graduates

LET THE JOURNEY BEGIN

Your career should not be a one-route wonder. It should be a journey. With open opportunities and different destinations. With constant support and continuous development.

Visit **www.rbs.com/graduates** and let the journey begin.

RBS
The Royal Bank of Scotland Group

Make it happen

Sainsbury's

Vacancies for around 100-120 graduates in 2006

- Finance
- Human Resources
- Logistics
- Marketing
- Purchasing
- Retailing

Starting salary for 2006
£22,000-£25,000

Universities Sainsbury's plans to visit in 2005-6

Bath, Belfast, Birmingham, Bristol, Cardiff, Durham, Essex, Lancaster, Leeds, Liverpool, London, Manchester, Newcastle, Nottingham, Sheffield, Southampton, Strathclyde, Surrey, Warwick.
Please check with your university careers service for details of events.

Application deadline
Year-round recruitment
See website for full details.

Contact Details

✉ sainsburys@reed.co.uk
☎ 020 8228 5109

Turn to page 192 now to request more information about Sainsbury's.

Sainsbury's is a leading FTSE 100 company – a very high-profile name in a very fast-moving market. Its supermarkets achieve sales of £16 billion a year, serve 14 million customers and employ 150,000 people. Inspired by a new management team – led by chief executive Justin King – the company is winning back market share. These exciting times are creating great opportunities for graduates.

Sainsbury's is looking for sharp, smart graduates who love the buzz of retail. They're after instinct as well as intellect; personality as well as professionalism. Above all the company wants exceptionally motivated people ready to add value to the business.

Graduate roles are in retail, finance, supply chain, marketing, human resources, buying, and product technology and development. Each scheme helps graduates to develop leadership qualities, gain practical business skills and increase their capabilities. Everyone works on real business issues from day one, so there's an enormous amount of responsibility and the chance to make a difference.

Life at Sainsbury's can be tough. Whether a graduate is working in a store, depot or office, some days will be physically and intellectually demanding. Graduates will have to quickly hone their understanding of customers and colleagues. And they'll need to develop a clear understanding of themselves too, working with others to identify their strengths and weaknesses and get the training they need to progress. Graduates must decide whether they have the drive, character and passion needed to help make Sainsbury's great again.

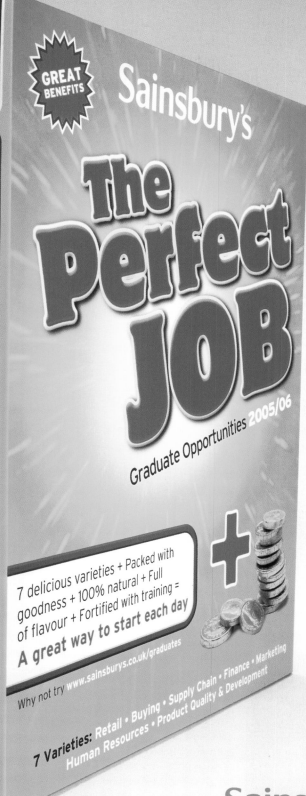

Sainsbury's

GREAT BENEFITS

The Perfect JOB

Graduate Opportunities 2005/06

7 delicious varieties + Packed with goodness + 100% natural + Full of flavour + Fortified with training = **A great way to start each day**

Why not try www.sainsburys.co.uk/graduates

7 Varieties: Retail • Buying • Supply Chain • Finance • Marketing • Human Resources • Product Quality & Development

Nutrition

Leadership
Develop your potential as an effective leader who can manage, coach and inspire.

Real experience
Learn what business is about inside a fast-moving company where you can make a difference.

Drive your career
Show your determination, energy and desire to deliver business results.

Community
Meet people, make connections and get the support of top management and colleagues.

Responsibility
Gain the confidence needed to make tough decisions that make a real difference.

Rewards
Get the rewards, training and opportunities you need to build a successful career.

FTSE 100
Revolutionise your CV by adding a truly household name.

Guarantee
We've set out to tell you what life at Sainsbury's is really like. No spin. No gloss. This is how it is.

Sainsbury's

www.sainsburys.co.uk/graduates

Vacancies for around 350 graduates in 2006

- Engineering
- Finance
- Human Resources
- IT
- Marketing
- Research & Development
- Sales

Vacancies also available in Europe

Starting salary for 2006
£27,500
UK minimum.

Universities that Shell plans to visit in 2005-6
Aberdeen, Bath, Birmingham, Bristol, Cambridge, Dublin, Durham, Edinburgh, Leeds, London, Loughborough, Manchester, Nottingham, Oxford, Sheffield, Southampton, Warwick.
Please check with your university careers service for details of events.

Application deadline
Year-round recruitment

Contact Details
✉ graduates@shell.com
☎ 0845 600 1819
Turn to page 192 now to request more information about Shell.

Shell is at the heart of the energy and petrochemical business and is one of the world's most successful organisations. They are totally committed to a business strategy that always balances profits with principles. They are also committed to attracting, training, developing and rewarding world class people for this truly world class business.

From the moment graduates join Shell, their development is of prime importance. Learning by doing, supported by their manager, is key – real responsibility and decision-making are part of life at Shell from day one. Career progression depends entirely on individual ability, talent and ambition.

Working for Shell, graduates could potentially move geographically, functionally and between different businesses. Shell have a strong ethic of promotion from within a global job opportunity intranet site to support this.

Graduates' academic records are one key factor in assessing applications, but Shell also place emphasis on performance during interviews and assessment centres. Shell have identified capacity, achievement and relationships as critical to high performance.

Shell have a number of pre-employment opportunities: the Shell Gourami Business Challenge, for which applications are welcome from finalists in Autumn 2005; placements, for which students in their penultimate year can apply during January and February 2006; and the Personal Development Award, for which applications are welcome from non-finalists in Spring 2006.

Full details on Shell can be found on their website, www.shell.com/careers.

EXPAND

Graduate Opportunities

Chemical, Petroleum, Mechanical, Process, Mining, Aeronautical, Electrical, Civil Engineering, Technology Consultancy & Research, IT, Sales & Marketing, Finance, HR

If you think you know Shell, think again. We may be well known for our petrochemicals business, but to become one of the world's leading energy companies takes a wide range of talented individuals. We are constantly changing and truly global – the opportunities are outstanding. Join us as a graduate and you will have the chance to diversify, specialise, develop your career internationally – even change direction completely. Whichever route you choose, you will start a real job with real responsibility.

You can expect full on-the-job and structured training, possibly leading to professional qualifications.

People from all disciplines looking for an international career are encouraged to apply (but anyone wanting to work within a technical role will need a relevant degree). Apply online or email graduates@shell.com for an application form.

Shell is an Equal Opportunity Employer.

www.shell.com/careers

Simmons & Simmons

Simmons & Simmons is a leading international law firm with over 1,000 legal staff in 20 business and financial centres across Europe, the Middle East, Asia and the US. They believe it is who they are and how they approach their work that sets them apart from their competition – and led to them being the only law firm given the Queen's Award in 2003.

Simmons & Simmons currently have sector groups focussing on Aerospace & Defence, Consumer Goods, Energy & Utilities, Financial Markets, Pharmaceutical & Biotechnology, Real Estate & Construction, Technology, Media & Telecommunications and Transport. The core practice areas, from which they draw their sector teams, are: Commercial, Corporate, Dispute Resolution, EU & Competition, Employment, Finance, IP, Projects, Real Estate & Environment and Tax.

They offer trainees high quality international experience and provide training, which equips their trainees with the insight and ability to deal with the legal and commercial issues relevant to their clients.

Simmons & Simmons look to recruit the right individuals, whether they have a law degree or non-law degree. Currently the firm is looking to recruit 50 trainees to commence training in September 2008/March 2009. Academic achievement is key but the firm also wants rounded individuals who can fit into their teams as their trainees will need to work with people in the firm's international offices and with clients throughout the world.

They also offer opportunities for students to sample their work on their summer vacation scheme.

Simmons & Simmons

To find out more about our training contracts or summer vacation schemes visit: **www.simmons-simmons.com.** Alternatively, contact Vickie Chamberlain, Graduate Recruitment Manager at **recruitment@simmons-simmons.com.**

Welcome to our world

SLAUGHTER AND MAY

Vacancies for around 85 graduates in 2006

For training courses starting in September 2008 and March 2009.

 Law

Starting salary for 2006
£29,500

Universities that Slaughter and May plans to visit in 2005-6

Please check with your university careers service for details of events.

Application deadline
Year-round recruitment
See website for full details.

Contact Details

✉ grad.recruit@
    slaughterandmay.com
 020 7600 1200

Turn to page 192 now to request more information about Slaughter and May.

Slaughter and May is a leading international law firm whose principal areas of practice are in the fields of corporate, commercial and financing law.

The firm's clients range from the world's leading multinationals to venture capital start-ups. They include public and private companies, governments and non-governmental organisations, commercial and investment banks. The lawyers devise solutions for complex, often transnational, problems and advise some of the world's brightest business minds.

Their overseas offices and close working relationships with leading independent law firms in other jurisdictions mean there are opportunities to work in places such as Amsterdam, Brussels, Berlin, Copenhagen, Düsseldorf, Frankfurt, Helsinki, Hong Kong, Luxembourg, Madrid, Milan, New York, Oslo, Paris, Prague, Rome, Singapore, Stockholm and Tokyo.

Approximately 85-95 training contracts are available per year for trainee solicitors. Slaughter and May also offers two-week placements during the Christmas, Easter and summer vacations for those considering a career in law.

Following Law School, there is a two year training period during which time trainee solicitors gain experience of a broad cross-section of the firm's practice by taking an active part in the work of four or five groups, sharing an office with a partner or experienced associate. In addition, Slaughter and May offers an extensive training programme of lectures, seminars and courses with discussion groups covering general and specialised legal topics.

Applications from undergraduates of good 2.1 ability from any discipline are considered. Please visit their website for further information.

Your period of training is, of course, very important. But in the context of your career, it's just the beginning. We also put a great deal of emphasis on helping you develop your longer-term career with Slaughter and May – in the practice area you choose.

Look forward in confidence.

SLAUGHTER AND MAY

LEARN MORE *about graduate traineeships and vacation placements at one of the world's most respected law firms by contacting:*

Charlotte Houghton, Slaughter and May, One Bunhill Row, London EC1Y 8YY. Telephone 020 7600 1200.

www.slaughterandmay.com

LEARNING TO LEAD

www.teachfirst.org.uk

Vacancies for around 300 graduates in 2006

☐ **All Sectors**

Starting salary for 2006
£Competitive

Universities Teach First plans to visit in 2005-6
Bath, Birmingham, Bristol, Cambridge, Durham, Edinburgh, Leeds, Liverpool, London, Manchester, Newcastle, Nottingham, Oxford, St Andrews, Sussex, Warwick,
Please check with your university careers service for details of events.

Application deadline
Varies by function
See website for full details.

Contact Details
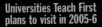 faq@teachfirst.org.uk
 020 7718 5570
Turn to page 192 now to request more information about Teach First.

Teach First transforms outstanding graduates into inspiring leaders, ready to excel in any management career. Combining intensive teacher training and experience with a unique leadership and management skills programme, Teach First is a unique opportunity both to be different and to make a difference.

High-profile recruiters from all sectors recognise that the skills and strategies developed in teaching are highly relevant and applicable to management careers. That is why over 80 companies, government agencies and public bodies are backing Teach First to develop top talent for the future.

Teach First recruits high-calibre graduates from all disciplines to train and qualify as teachers. Before being assigned to a school, participants attend six weeks of intensive teacher training. At the end of year one, graduates achieve Qualified Teacher Status, a qualification that means they can return to the teaching profession at any point in the future.

Alongside teaching, participants also follow the innovative Foundations of Leadership course, designed and delivered in collaboration with Teach First business supporters and Tanaka Business School at Imperial College.

Joining Teach First means spending two years teaching in a challenging London or Manchester school, preparing and delivering real lessons to real pupils. It is uniquely demanding but also uniquely rewarding. Few other career choices offer the same degree of responsibility so early or the chance to make such an important difference. And after Teach First? Whether participants choose finance, management, public service or education, they stand out as exceptional individuals with something special to offer.

I taught first.

Teachers are leaders – they have to be. When you're standing in front of a class of 30 students, many from challenging backgrounds, it's up to you to find a way to engage, inspire, communicate and guide. It's the same in management. That's why over 80 leading employers, from all sectors, are backing Teach First to develop the leaders of the future.

Teach First's unique two-year graduate training programme combines intensive teacher training and experience with an innovative management skills and leadership course, while our supporters provide unparalleled internship, networking and coaching opportunities.

This is your chance to be different and to make a difference. Whatever you aim to do with your career, Teach First.

Teach First
LEARNING TO LEAD

Find out more and apply online at www.teachfirst.org.uk

TESCO

www.tesco.com/debut

Vacancies for around 150 graduates in 2006

- General Management
- Human Resources
- IT
- Marketing
- Media
- Purchasing
- Research & Development
- Retailing

Starting salary for 2006
£21,500

Universities that Tesco plans to visit in 2005-6

Aston, Bath, Leicester, London, Loughborough, Manchester, Nottingham, Reading, Sheffield, Southampton, Strathclyde, Swansea, Warwick.
Please check with your university careers service for details of events.

Application deadline
Varies by function
See website for full details

Contact Details
✉ graduate.recruitment@ uk.tesco.com

Turn to page 192 now to request more information about Tesco.

Multi-national, market-leading, fast-moving and challenging – who knows where graduates will end up at Tesco!

With over 1700 stores and 230,000 employees, Tesco is the country's largest private sector employer, and is experiencing rapid international expansion. Furthermore, Tesco is committed to being as successful in non food as it is in food: Tesco.com is the world's most successful on-line retailer; stores continually expand their range offering customers new products and services from mobile phones to financial services.

Tesco look for graduates with a unique blend of people, leadership and analytical skills. They need a passion for the industry and the ability to rise to the challenge of working in the exciting world of retail. Able to make decisions quickly, graduates should be flexible in their approach and comfortable with Tesco's demanding, ever-changing but ultimately supportive environment. Graduates benefit from exposure to all areas of the business as well as hands-on experience mixed with workshops, theory and personal skills development.

Tesco recruit into three programmes: Store Management sees graduates progress to store manager within five years and be responsible for up to 800 staff and a £50 million turnover; in the Specialist Management Programmes graduates join a key function such as Personnel, Property, Tesco.com, Insight, developing in-depth knowledge; and in the General Management programmes, graduates focus on becoming retail business managers in areas such as Commercial, Corporate and Legal Affairs and Marketing.

Tesco offer annual career planning and a continually revised personal development plan offering opportunities to transfer to other functions.

WHAT COULD THE UK'S NO. 1 RETAILER POSSIBLY OFFER GRADUATES?

GRADUATE SCHEME

Exposure. Development. Networking. International career options. Basically, the list goes on and on. There are high-profile graduate opportunities within every area of our cutting-edge global business, from Personnel, Finance and Corporate Purchasing, to Property, Tesco.com, Corporate & Legal Affairs, Commercial and our Insight Unit.

If you think we're just a supermarket, there's so much that you're missing. Find out more at www.tesco.com/debut

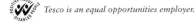 *Tesco is an equal opportunities employer.* **www.tesco.com/debut**

TESCO

UBS

www.ubs.com/graduates

Vacancies for around 120-150 graduates in 2006

- Finance
- Human Resources
- Investment Banking
- IT
- Logistics

Starting salary for 2006
£Competitive

Universities that UBS plans to visit in 2005-6
Please check with your university careers service for details of events.

Application deadline
11th November 2005
See website for full details.

Contact Details
Turn to page 192 now to request more information about UBS.

UBS is one of the world's leading financial firms, serving a discerning global client base. As an organization, it combines financial strength with a global culture that embraces change.

They offer a working environment of mutual respect and support for the best and the brightest people. Their culture values and rewards individual initiative, open mind and client focus. There is a complete range of opportunities in all areas of their business.

A graduate's personality and intellect are more important than academic discipline. Best-in-class training and development build the skills and competencies to enable graduates to excel in their chosen role. Ambition and application determine the speed at which graduates progress.

At every stage of a UBS career, top-quality education and development resources support them in achieving their goals. UBS's world-class training captures potential and helps graduates hit the ground running. Programme flexibility enables graduates to create an individual education path that meets shared objectives. Responsibility increases with achievements.

UBS's global client relationships are built on intimate understanding, so views and opinions are important. Graduates will contribute toward the decisions that power UBS's growth. Above all, UBS want graduates to be successful. The alignment of career aspirations and business objectives promotes the creation of lasting value for both graduates and UBS.

UBS offers talented undergraduates with outstanding educational credentials the opportunity to apply for their academic sponsorship programme from October 2005. Please visit www.ubs.com/academicsponsorship.

Your performance drives our outstanding results. It starts with you.

What keeps UBS at the forefront of global financial services? Your skills, commitment and ambition to be the best. Our innovation comes from your creativity and appetite for challenge. The ideas you share with colleagues help develop the products and services that sustain our market leadership positions across Europe, the Americas and Asia Pacific. A dynamic and diverse environment provides you with every opportunity to fulfill your potential and further our achievements. Industry-leading training programs help you to hit the ground running. How far you go is up to you.

Find out more about graduate opportunities and life at UBS at **www.ubs.com/graduates.**

| Wealth Management | Global Asset Management | Investment Bank |

You & Us

Unilever

We believe 'dirt is good.'
Not surprisingly were looking
for people who aren't afraid
to get their hands dirty.

**Vacancies for around
50 graduates in 2006**

- Engineering
- Finance
- Human Resources
- IT
- Marketing
- Sales

Starting salary for 2006
£25,500

**Universities that Unilever
plans to visit in 2005-6**

Aston, Bath, Birmingham,
Cambridge, Durham,
Edinburgh, Leeds,
London, Manchester,
Newcastle, Nottingham,
Oxford, Sheffield,
Strathclyde, Warwick.
Please check with your university
careers service for details of events.

Application deadline
16th December 2005
See website for full details.

Contact Details
✉ enquiry@unilever
graduates.com
☎ 0870 154 3550

Turn to page 192 now to request
more information about Unilever.

Unilever is a leading consumer goods company, making and marketing products in the foods, home and personal care sectors across the world.

In fact over half the families in the world use brands such as Dove, Magnum, Knorr, Persil and Lynx every day. Unilever's mission is to add vitality to life – by helping people feel good, look good and get more out of life. Behind every successful brand lie a number of complex challenges, in all areas of the business: these are what graduates at Unilever will tackle.

Unilever's graduate development scheme is designed to help graduates reach senior management. Graduates join a specific function in Unilever, where they have a real job with key deliverables and responsibilities from the outset.

Generally, the scheme includes four placements within two years and mobility is essential to get the breadth of experience required. There is excellent training covering leadership development, general business and professional skills. Full support is offered to gain Chartered status or relevant professional qualifications, such as CIPD, CIMA, ImechE, IChemE and IEE.

Unilever wants people with the potential to lead its business. To do this, graduates need to be passionate about business, inspired by profit, competition and customer satisfaction, as well as able to behave with integrity showing both ambition and entrepreneurial spirit.

Unilever's high quality training programmes help graduates develop the expertise and personal qualities they need in order to achieve their career goals. They offer a vast range of opportunities that just have to be taken.

For more information, please visit www.unilever.co.uk/careers

We're looking for people who believe this is the best place to dump four million plastic detergent bottles.

...ore the breathtaking scenery of Yellowstone Park for a second and ...nk about how over four million plastic detergent bottles are helping ...serve its beauty. We've created a boardwalk with these bottles to help ...de you through the park. If you too can see creative solutions where ...ers just see problems you'll enjoy a challenging career at Unilever so ...t www.unilever.com/ourcompany/careers

Could it be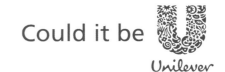

WPP

Vacancies for around 1-10 graduates in 2006

■ Marketing
■ Media

Starting salary for 2006
£22,000-£27,000

Universities that WPP plans to visit in 2005-6
Bristol, Cambridge, Edinburgh, London, Oxford.
Please check with your university careers service for details of events.

Application deadline
18th November 2005

Contact Details

✉ hmiller@wpp.com
☎ 020 7408 2204

Turn to page 192 now to request more information about WPP.

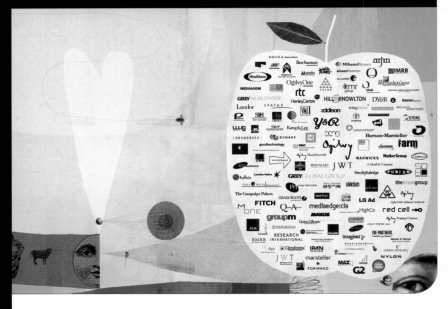

WPP is one of the world's leading communications services groups, made up of leading companies in advertising, media investment management, information, insight & consultancy, public relations & public affairs, branding & identity, healthcare communications, direct, promotion & relationship marketing and specialist communications.

Through its companies, WPP provides communications services to national, multinational and global clients, including many Fortune 500 and FTSE 100 companies. Its 84,000 people work out of 2,000 offices in 106 countries.

WPP Marketing Fellowships, which develop high-calibre management talent with experience across a range of marketing disciplines, will be awarded to applicants who graduate in 2005 or 2006 and have yet to embark on a full time career. Those selected will work in a number of WPP companies and across different marketing disciplines.

WPP is offering several three-year Fellowships, unique multi-disciplinary experience, competitive remuneration and excellent long term career prospects within WPP. It wants people who are committed to marketing, who take a rigorous and creative approach to problem-solving, who are intellectually curious and will function well in a flexible, loosely structured work environment.

The first year of the Fellowship is spent working in a WPP sponsoring company and a personal mentor is assigned to provide overall career guidance. Thereafter, each individual will spend 18 to 24 months working in one or two other WPP companies, with each chosen on the basis of the individual's interests and the Group's needs.

WPP

Marketing Fellowships 2006

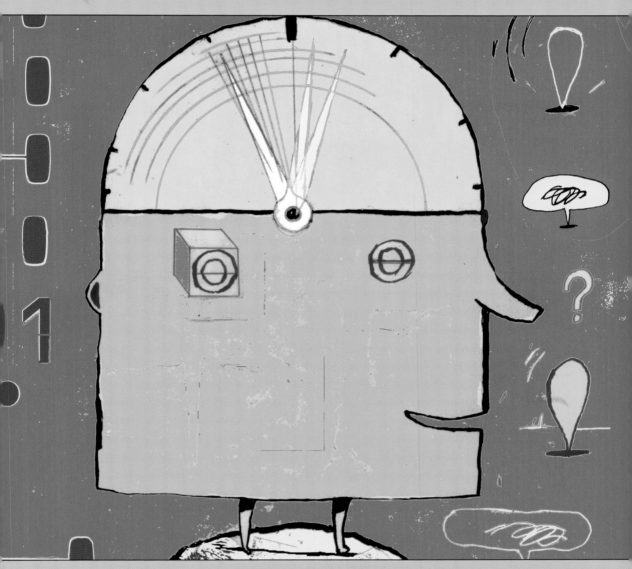

Ambidextrous brains required

[W]PP is one of the world's leading communications services groups. [M]ajor brands include J. Walter Thompson, Ogilvy & Mather, [Yo]ung & Rubicam, Grey Global Group, Red Cell, MindShare, [M]ediaedge:cia, Millward Brown, OgilvyOne, Wunderman, Hill & [Kn]owlton, Burson-Marsteller, Ogilvy Public Relations, Cohn & Wolfe, [Co]mmonHealth, Enterprise IG and Landor, among others.

[Th]eir specialist skills include Advertising, Media investment [man]agement, Information, insight & consultancy, Public relations [&] public affairs, Branding & identity, Healthcare communications,

Direct, promotion & relationship marketing and Specialist communications: disparate disciplines with two common factors. They are all in business to contribute to the success of their clients. And they all do so through a demanding combination of flair and slog; intuition and logic; left brain and right brain.

WPP will consider applicants who graduate in 2005 or 2006 and have yet to embark on a full time career. Those selected will work in a number of WPP companies and across different marketing disciplines. Excellent long-term career prospects within a WPP company.

[In]formation leaflets are available from:
[H]arriet Miller at WPP, 27 Farm Street, London W1J 5RJ
[T] +44(0)20 7408 2204 F +44(0)20 7493 6819
[E]mail: hmiller@wpp.com

Deadline for entry: 18 November 2005
visit our website and apply online at
www.wpp.com

Enter our prize draw to win £5,000 in cash or an iPod Shuffle!

Make use of our free information service to find out more about the employers featured within this edition of **The Times Top 100 Graduate Employers,** and you could be £5,000 richer when you start your first job!

All you need to do is complete the special **Information Request** card that appears opposite and send it back before the closing date, **31st March 2006.**

Or you can register your details online at **www.Top100GraduateEmployers.com**

Every completed request card or online registration will be entered into a special prize draw to win the £5,000 in cash. There are also **50 iPod Shuffles** to be won – one at each of the universities at which the *Top 100* book is distributed, for those who reply by **30th November 2005.**

The information that you request will be despatched to you from the employers directly. The service is entirely free to all UK students and recent graduates.

Fill in the card or go to www.Top100GraduateEmployers.com now!

THE TIMES

TOP 100

GRADUATE EMPLOYERS

INFORMATION REQUEST 2005/2006

To request further information about any of the employers featured in The Times Top 100 Graduate Employers and enter our free prize draw to win £5,000, just complete your details and return this postcard.

Your information will be despatched to you directly from the employers, either by email, post or text message via your mobile phone.

NAME _____

UNIVERSITY _____

COURSE _____

TERMTIME ADDRESS

_____

_____

_____

EMAIL_____

MOBILE TEL. NO. _____

Please tick the sectors that you would most like to work in:

ACCOUNTANCY . . . . ❏
CONSULTING . . . . ❏
ENGINEERING . . . . ❏
FINANCE . . . . ❏
GENERAL MANAGEMENT . . . ❏
HUMAN RESOURCES . . . . ❏
INVESTMENT BANKING . . . . . ❏
IT . . . . ❏
LAW . . . . ❏
LOGISTICS . . . . ❏
MANUFACTURING . . . . ❏
MARKETING . . . . ❏
MEDIA . . . . ❏
PURCHASING . . . . ❏
RESEARCH & DEVELOPMENT . ❏
RETAILING . . . . ❏
SALES . . . . ❏

❏ PRE-FINAL YEAR   ❏ FINAL YEAR   ❏ I'VE ALREADY GRADUATED

The closing date to request information from these employers and be included in the prize draw to win £5,000 is **Friday 31st March 2006.** If you do **not** wish to be included on our general mailing list and receive information from other relevant graduate employers, please tick here ❏

Please tick the organisations you would like information from:

ABN AMRO . . . . ❏	HBOS . . . . ❏
ACCENTURE . . . . ❏	HSBC . . . . ❏
AIRBUS . . . . ❏	IBM . . . . ❏
ALDI . . . . ❏	ICI . . . . ❏
ALLEN & OVERY . . . . ❏	JP MORGAN . . . . ❏
ARCADIA . . . . ❏	KPMG . . . . ❏
ARMY . . . . ❏	LINKLATERS . . . . ❏
ASDA . . . . ❏	LLOYDS TSB . . . . ❏
ASTRAZENECA . . . . ❏	L'ORÉAL . . . . ❏
ATKINS . . . . ❏	MARKS & SPENCER . . . . ❏
BAE SYSTEMS . . . . ❏	MARS . . . . ❏
BAKER & MCKENZIE . . . . ❏	McDONALD'S RESTAURANTS . ❏
BARCLAYS BANK . . . . ❏	MERCER HR CONSULTING . . ❏
BARCLAYS CAPITAL . . . . ❏	MERRILL LYNCH . . . . ❏
BBC . . . . ❏	METROPOLITAN POLICE . . . . ❏
BRITISH NUCLEAR GROUP . . ❏	MI5 - THE SECURITY SERVICE ❏
BT . . . . ❏	MICROSOFT . . . . ❏
CADBURY SCHWEPPES . . . . . ❏	MINISTRY OF DEFENCE . . . . . ❏
CANCER RESEARCH UK . . . . ❏	MORGAN STANLEY . . . . ❏
CITIGROUP . . . . ❏	NGDP FOR LOCAL GOVERNMENT ❏
CIVIL SERVICE FAST STREAM . ❏	NHS . . . . ❏
CLIFFORD CHANCE . . . . ❏	OXFAM . . . . ❏
CORUS . . . . ❏	PA CONSULTING . . . . ❏
CREDIT SUISSE FIRST BOSTON ❏	POLICE HPDS . . . . ❏
DATA CONNECTION . . . . ❏	PRICEWATERHOUSECOOPERS ❏
DELOITTE . . . . ❏	PROCTER & GAMBLE . . . . . . ❏
DEUTSCHE BANK . . . . ❏	QINETIQ . . . . ❏
DIAGEO . . . . ❏	REUTERS . . . . ❏
DLA PIPER RUDNICK	ROLLS-ROYCE . . . . ❏
GRAY CARY . . . . ❏	ROYAL BANK OF SCOTLAND GP ❏
DSTL . . . . ❏	SAINSBURY'S . . . . ❏
ERNST & YOUNG . . . . ❏	SHELL . . . . ❏
EVERSHEDS . . . . ❏	SIMMONS & SIMMONS . . . . . ❏
EXXON MOBIL . . . . ❏	SLAUGHTER AND MAY . . . . . ❏
FRESHFIELDS BRUCKHAUS	TEACH FIRST . . . . ❏
DERINGER . . . . ❏	TESCO . . . . ❏
GCHQ . . . . ❏	UBS . . . . ❏
GLAXOSMITHKLINE . . . . ❏	UNILEVER . . . . ❏
GOLDMAN SACHS . . . . ❏	WPP . . . . ❏

THE INSTITUTE OF CHARTERED ACCOUNTANTS IN ENGLAND & WALES ❏